london
transport
museum

Depot
Discovery

Plan of the Depot showing the location
of themed collections on the ground
floor, and upper levels (circled).
Please note, the Depot is a working
store and visitors should therefore take
care when walking around this site.

See page 101 for enlarged plan.

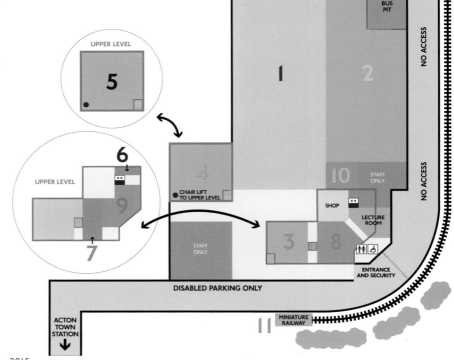

Published in 2015
London Transport Museum
Covent Garden Piazza
London WC2E 7BB
Tel +44 (0)343 222 5000

First published 2015
Reprinted with amendments 2019

All images are © TfL, from the London Transport Museum
collection, except where noted.

Text by London Transport Museum
Design by LTM Design

ISBN 978-1-871829-24-2

ltmuseum.co.uk
Registered charity number 1123122

Contents

Welcome to Depot Discovery by Museum Director — 04

01   Rail vehicles — 06

02   Road vehicles — 14

03   Engineering and technology — 28

04   Design and environment — 38

05   Maps, signs and furniture — 46

06   Small object store — 52

07   Library and ephemera — 60

08   Plans and drawings — 68

09   Posters and artwork — 76

10   Photography, film and sound — 84

11   Miniature railway — 90

London Transport Museum Friends — 91

Shopping at the Depot — 92

Museum as a charity — 93

London Transport Museum at Covent Garden — 94

Discover more — 96

Glossary — 98

Plan your discovery — 100

Welcome to
Depot Discovery

This book is your guide to the hidden
treasures of the London Transport Museum.
We hope you will dip in and discover
something new about our collections,
or learn more about familiar objects.

When the Museum Depot at Acton opened in October 1999, it was the UK's first museum store designed to allow regular public access. Although other museums have since followed, the Depot still provides an unusual opportunity to go behind the scenes to view the full breadth of the most comprehensive collection of historic urban transport material in the world.

The Depot is of course first and foremost our working storehouse, a secure and environmentally stable home for those collections which are not on display in the Museum. Here our curators and volunteers record, manage and protect the collections. Vehicle restoration is also undertaken, although intensive engineering work is mostly contracted to specialist partners elsewhere.

Alongside the essential collections care, public access is a regular feature through our open weekends, monthly guided tours, group visits and admission for researchers, film-makers and photographers. Project work with schools, community groups and young people also takes place here, using the collections to encourage learning and creativity, and to inspire the curators, designers and engineers of the future.

Unlike a traditional museum gallery, the Depot does not have panels of text or a particular route to follow, nor are the objects arranged in chronological order. To enjoy the Depot you must become an explorer and this guide will help you to understand the treasures you unearth. This includes some of the Museum's stars alongside less-well known but equally important objects. Depot Discovery is divided into a number of themes which correspond roughly to the arrangement of objects at the Depot. These are outlined on the Depot plan on page 101.

With over 320,000 accessioned items in the Museum collection there is plenty to discover and new objects are being acquired all the time. The Depot's 6,000 square metres contain some 100 road and rail vehicles, over 5,000 poster designs, 2,000 artworks, 93,000 photographs and 45,000 plans and drawings. There are enamel maps and signs, uniforms, models, architectural fragments, textiles, crockery, sports trophies, timetables, tickets and all the paraphernalia of the world's oldest mass transit system. Iconic items such as the 1938 Tube train, early examples of Henry Beck's Tube map, the prototype Routemaster and the original artwork for Edward McKnight Kauffer's *Power* poster sit alongside unsung heroes such as lift motors, bus engines, uniforms, signal frames, station roundels, clocks and ticket machines. There are quirky items too: the tram trailer that became a cottage, a fancy dress costume covered in bus tickets and a London Transport Christmas pudding. We also borrow vehicles, and let other museums and heritage organisations use the Depot to display their own collections, so no two visits are ever the same.

Our collections are stored in a way that is best for their long-term preservation, while as far as possible making them accessible for visitors to see and enjoy. The road and rail vehicles need a big dry shed with platforms for easy access. Film and photographic negatives require cool storage, while the posters are stored flat in plastic sleeves in stable conditions of temperature and humidity. The massive motors and drums of Underground lift gear are stored together based on size and purpose. Enamel maps and signs are wired to mesh walls so they can be seen more easily and artworks are on mobile racks. Small, delicate objects are kept in glass-fronted lockable units. The Museum Depot is truly an Aladdin's cave of London memorabilia, although in the interest of conservation we ask you not to rub the lamps!

Sam Mullins, Director,
London Transport Museum

1998/89882

Our extensive collection of rail vehicles (or railway rolling stock) at the Depot shows the development of trains for the London Underground from the late 19th century to the present day. You can see the whole vehicle collection, road and rail, in **Collections online** on the Museum website.

The earliest rail vehicles at the Depot were operating in the 1890s and we continue to add more as they retire from service. London Underground trains come in two basic sizes. The larger 'sub-surface' stock, used on the Metropolitan, District, Circle and Hammersmith & City lines, is similar in size to mainline and Overground suburban trains. They are typically named with a letter such as 'A-stock' or 'C-stock'. The other Underground lines use trains which fit the smaller diameter deep Tube tunnels. They are typically named after the first year of their manufacture, for example '1938-stock'. The difference in size is particularly noticeable where District and Piccadilly line trains run alongside each other outside the Depot between Acton Town and Hammersmith.

Q stock cars 08063, 1935; 4416 and 4417, 1938 →

Q stock trains were a staple of District line services from 1938 to 1971. They were formed of a mix of cars in different combinations, with different motor cars and different styles of coach. Some featured American-style clerestory roofs dating back to 1923. These older cars retained their traditional appearance, but were upgraded and modified with automatic doors and pneumatic brakes, to run with the new Q38 cars. The new stock was strikingly modern in comparison, with sleek, flared sides and smooth, curved roofs, and interior styling similar to the 1938 Tube stock. After withdrawal in 1971, one of the 1923 trailer cars (known as Q23 stock) was preserved and is on display at the Museum in Covent Garden. Two Q38 motor cars were used for shunting duties at Ruislip depot, and one clerestory roof Q35 car was bought by the London Underground Railway Society. LTM acquired these three cars in the 1990s.

1998/57307, 1998/58918

1998/58918

1998/57307

‘

Q stock cars, 1935 and 1938

The ambitious project to restore the Q stock began in 2016. Funded by London Transport Museum Friends and public donations, the aim is to bring a three-car train into operational condition. The cars will be restored to different periods, to explore a range of themes and stories, from wartime to the post-war years of austerity and rebuilding, and the prosperity of the 1950s and 60s. Most of the restoration work is carried out by volunteers at the Museum's Depot at Acton. They work on everything from sanding and painting, through to electrical work and producing technical drawings. A big challenge has been rewiring the lighting circuits in the passenger saloons to run on today's lower track voltages. Another task has involved research to establish the correct moquette seat covering to use in each car that is right for the period. The price tag for different, small runs of moquette fabric can be more than £300 per seat.

Katariina Maurenen, Curator
London Transport Museum

’

1997/7453

Metropolitan Railway trailer car, 1904

This trailer car from one of the first Metropolitan electric trains was introduced on the Baker Street to Uxbridge service in 1905. Since the Underground went electric in the early 1900s, each unit in a train has always been called a car, rather than a coach or a carriage, following American usage. This car was part of a train with motors and a driving cab at each end and trailers in between. These used the revolutionary multiple unit control system devised by Frank Sprague in the USA, first used in Chicago in 1898. This allowed an electric train to be driven from either end without needing a separate locomotive for power. Early British electric units like this introduced an American look to the transport system, with a single open saloon instead of individual compartments. The car which survives in our collection is in a very poor state and is awaiting funds for restoration.

1997/7453

1998/61311

You can see examples of early electrical infrastructure in our Engineering and technology collection, including the enormous mercury arc rectifier on page 37.

1996/797

Standard stock car No. 3327, 1927

This driving motor car is an example of the 1,466 Tube cars known as 'Standard stock' built between 1922 and 1934, which replaced 'Gate stock' (see page 12). Standard referred to their compatibility with cars from different manufacturers and the press referred to them as 'Tube cars deluxe'. They had air-powered doors, improved lighting and were the mainstay of trains on the Northern, Bakerloo, Piccadilly and Central lines until the late 1930s. In reduced numbers they operated on the Piccadilly and Central lines until the early 1960s. The control equipment was housed in a compartment behind the driving cab, so passengers could hear the electrical contacts working as the train accelerated. This vehicle was originally acquired by the Science Museum with sections opened up so people could see how various items of equipment worked. It was transferred to London Transport Museum in 1996.

1996/797

2003/17108

2002/18939

1991/20

Electric Sleet Locomotive, 1939

Some Underground cars have an extended life after passenger service when they are converted to a new use as a maintenance vehicle. This Electric Sleet Locomotive (ESL No.107) was built at Acton Works in 1939 by combining parts from two former Tube driving motor cars. They were originally built for the Central London Railway (now the Central line) in 1903. In the central section were tanks of anti-freeze which were brushed on to the electrical conductor rails to clear ice, sleet and snow on cold days. ESL No.107 was used for this essential seasonal duty until the 1990s when de-icing equipment was fitted as standard to modern passenger trains.

1991/20

1998/33667

R-stock District line driving car, 1952 →

This driving car from the first unpainted silver-aluminium train on the Underground, was introduced on the District line in 1953. During the Second World War London Transport's works were used to build bomber aircraft, providing the Underground's engineers with a wealth of experience regarding the use of lightweight materials and construction methods. From the early 1950s, new Underground trains were given aluminium alloy bodies which were lighter than steel. This saved on power and, as aluminium does not rust, the trains could be left unpainted. Our car was in the last R-stock train to run on the Underground (see photo above) and was retired in 1983.

1982/35

1982/35

 After the Second World War, new technology such as this was also applied to London's buses, including the Routemasters which can be seen in the Road vehicle collection.

2001/16301

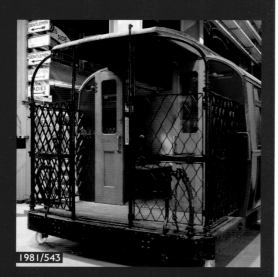
1981/543

Piccadilly Tube Gate stock car section, 1909

⬆

A section from an original steel-bodied car built for the Great Northern, Piccadilly & Brompton Railway, now the Piccadilly line, which opened in 1906. Each car had narrow sliding doors from an open platform at either end, where a gateman rode. His job was to call out station names and open and close the metal platform gates to let passengers on and off at stations. It was a slow and cumbersome process, especially in rush hour. In the 1920s new trains with multiple air-powered doors all controlled by one guard replaced Gate stock on all Tube lines, making the service faster and easier to operate.

1981/543

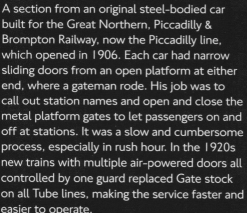
2003/3155

1938 Tube stock four-car train

⬇

These trains are regarded by many as the classic London Tube trains, which set a design benchmark in the late 1930s and carried millions of Londoners for 50 years. The exterior bodywork is smooth and semi-streamlined. To create more space for passengers inside each car, all the train's control equipment was relocated under the floor. The interior layout and fittings were designed to make a journey more relaxing and comfortable even when the train was crowded. The seats and lighting are in the Art Deco style. Our four-car set was in service until 1988 and has been restored to full working order so that visitors can experience Tube travel as it was in the mid-20th century. Please check our website for details of the next outing of the 'Art Deco special'.

1991/213

1991/213

2003/20443

Victoria line Tube stock driving car, 1967 →

Queen Elizabeth II travelled in this car when she opened the Victoria line in 1969. These new automatic silver trains were given a contemporary, high-tech look with twin headlamps and wraparound cab windows. At the time of opening, the Victoria line was the most advanced underground railway in the world with computers driving the trains between stations. In the 1990s, every train was painted and completely refurbished with a redesigned interior layout. These original trains were replaced by new rolling stock in 2012.

2010/23833

2010/23833

2014/3375

2011/11258

Metropolitan Railway milk van No. 3, 1896

This van was used to transport milk into London from farms in Hertfordshire and Buckinghamshire. I love the care which was clearly taken with the van's appearance, with wood panelling and the hand-painted Metropolitan Railway coat of arms. Although it is not as intricate as the beautifully restored Carriage 353, it is easy to imagine the two forming part of the same train, with the milk van comfortably holding its own. With ventilation to keep the milk fresh and modified suspension to prevent it from turning to butter during the journey, the milk van also demonstrates the engineering solutions required even for seemingly simple tasks.

David Southworth, Volunteer family-tour guide London Transport Museum

1981/540

02 Road vehicles

2004/6538

In 1900, horse power ruled the roads in London, but just a few years later new types of mechanical power were being applied to trams, buses and taxis. Our collection at the Depot demonstrates the rapid mechanisation of the city's public transport in the early 20th century. You can see all the vehicles in the Museum collection, both rail and road, on the Museum website.

First there were electric trams, then different types of petrol-driven motor bus were introduced and by 1914 their horse-drawn predecessors had vanished from London's streets. In the 1930s, electric trolleybuses began to replace trams and more efficient engines were introduced for buses. By 1952 all London's tramways had closed, and by 1962 all buses operated by London Transport were diesel-powered. Modern electric trams reappeared in Croydon in 2000 with the opening of the Tramlink system. Today, London's buses use a mixture of all-electric, fuel cell and hybrid diesel-electric power.

1981/526

Garden seat horse bus, c1890

There were thousands of horse buses like this in Victorian London. This example was owned by the London General Omnibus Company (LGOC), which ran the largest bus fleet in the city. The LGOC built its own buses at the company's coachworks in Islington. Each wooden vehicle was hand-built to a standard design, and could carry up to 26 passengers. This was the maximum load that two horses could cope with. Every bus on a particular route was painted in the same livery but there were no route numbers, so passengers had to identify their bus by its colour.

1981/526

2010/5001

2010/24377

E/1 type electric tram, 1910

The E/1 is the standard double deck tramcar used by the London County Council (LCC). The LCCT ran one of the largest tram networks in the world from the early 1900s. The motorman (driver) originally had to drive the tram in all weathers standing on an open platform. Windscreens were fitted in the 1920s but the drivers were never provided with a seat. Our tram was number 1025 in the London Transport fleet from 1933 , remaining in service until the end of London's trams in 1952. It still carries the headlamp cowl, or cover, fitted to meet blackout restrictions during the Second World War.

1981/530

1981/530

1981/514

B type motor bus B 340, 1911

The B type was London's first reliable mass-produced motor bus, designed for the London General Omnibus Company (LGOC) in 1910. Their engine units and chassis were built at a factory in Walthamstow by the Associated Equipment Company, which became the main supplier of London buses until the 1960s. The B type was sturdy and cheap to make, the bus equivalent of Henry Ford's famous Model T car. In less than two years the LGOC was able to replace its entire horse bus fleet with B type motor buses and operate them over much longer routes.

When the First World War broke out in 1914, London buses found a new use as troop transports for the British Army. Many were sent straight from the streets of the Capital to the Western Front.

The Museum has two B type buses and as part of the First World War commemorations in 2014, our 1913 bus B 2737 was restored to its wartime appearance. Our other bus B 340, which dates from 1911, is painted in the red livery of the LGOC (top left).

1981/514

2013/10256

1998/89290

1994/146

LT type single deck motor bus, 1931

This is the single deck version of the LT type, used mainly on suburban and hilly routes. It was known as the 'Scooter' by bus crews. After years of service on the London streets, this bus was sold to become a holiday home. It was in very poor condition when it first came to the Museum, but was rebuilt and restored to working order in 2002 with funding from the London Transport Museum Friends (see page 91) and the Transport Trust. Reconstructing the interior and seating required some detective work, as we only had black and white photographs and a watercolour impression for reference.

1994/146

1998/88048

1981/527

1998/84546

A1 type trolleybus, 1931

This is a unique survivor - the very first electric trolleybus used in London from 1931 until 1948. A trolleybus is a cross between a tram and a bus. It has an electric motor supplied with power from overhead wires but instead of running on fixed rails, like a tram, it runs on rubber tyres and can be steered like a bus. Faced with the high cost of modernising the trams and rails in the 1930s, London United Tramways (LUT) decided to replace its network of vehicles in the south west suburbs with trolleybuses which were cheaper to build. This type of trolleybus became known as the 'Diddler'. Two explanations for the nickname exist — one is that trolleybuses, unlike trams which were fixed, could wander or 'diddle' about the road. The alternative suggestion is that people felt cheated or 'diddled' when a trolleybus turned up rather than a tram! The photograph (left) shows a 'Diddler' on the final day of trolleybus operation, 8 May 1962.

1981/527

1998/58964

AEC Mercury tower wagon, 1936

Tower wagons were essential service vehicles for maintaining the tram and trolleybus network, working mostly at night. The cab had space for a repair crew and their equipment. The telescopic tower and platform gave the men access to overhead wires. During the Second World War crews often worked on these towers restoring damaged power lines while the Blitz raged around them. Our vehicle, 89Q, was built by the Associated Equipment Company (AEC) in 1936 and used by London Transport until the trolleybus system was fully replaced by the motor bus in 1962. It was sold to become a breakdown truck and the wooden tower was removed. We acquired the vehicle in1985 and restored it to its original condition, with a rebuilt, fully operational tower.

1991/21

1991/21

2010/3754

Taximeter road testing trailer, c1950

This taximeter trailer measured road distances, to make sure taxi passengers were being charged the correct fare. It was used by the Metropolitan Police, Public Carriage Office (PCO). Taxis would be fitted with a taximeter of the owner's choice, to calculate the distance and fare. The cab was then sent out with the meter running, over stretches of road near the PCO offices that had been measured exactly by the trailer. This allowed the PCO to check that the meter in the cab was accurately clocking the distance travelled.

2010/3754

1981/515

K type motor bus, 1920

After the First World War, there was a serious shortage of buses in London as many had been requisitioned for the war effort. The main successor to the B type was the larger K type, introduced in 1919, which seated 46 instead of 34 passengers. These buses were built by AEC in Walthamstow and were the first to use the large new central repair and overhaul works opened by the London General Omnibus Company (LGOC) at Chiswick in 1921. Although this bus may look primitive, with its open cab, top deck and solid rubber tyres, the ride still feels remarkably similar to a modern open-top bus. Our K type is in full operational order and completed the London to Brighton historic commercial vehicle run in 2002.

1981/515

1998/74687

GS type bus, 1953

The GS bus was the replacement for the Leyland Cub, which served low-traffic routes from 1934. London Transport ordered 84 GS type one-man operated buses for the Country Area, the first of which were delivered in 1953. The distinctive American Indian Chief crest on the bonnet was the trademark of Guy Motors, the company that produced the chassis. The Museum's bus GS 64 was first registered in December 1953 and allocated to Amersham Garage. It was in service at various locations up to 1967 and then stored until 1971 when it was sold for private use as a staff bus. It was eventually purchased by the Museum in 1985 and restoration began in 1986. This was completed in 1997.

1985/93

1985/93

GS type bus, 1953

A bus often looks like a bulky box on wheels. Turning it into a visually appealing vehicle which is practical but looks good on the street is a real design challenge. My vote for the most attractive bus in the museum collection goes to the GS type Guy Special, designed in 1953 for LT's lightly used country routes. The bus has a short body with a graceful curved profile rather than sharp angles, a traditional bonnet with the Indian Chief mascot of Guy Motors and the smart Lincoln Green colour scheme of London Transport Country Buses. It looks every bit as stylish as the sleek Jaguar sports cars of the period.

Oliver Green, Research Fellow
London Transport Museum

1989/119

Prototype Routemaster bus RM1, 1954

The Routemaster (RM) is probably the most famous bus in the world. London Transport engineers spent five years developing and testing their ideal vehicle for London using several prototypes before mass production began in 1958. The first prototype, RM1, went through various design changes. The Routemaster has a sturdy but lightweight aluminium body frame without a chassis. In the production version, all parts were interchangeable between Routemasters, making them simple to maintain. The braking and suspension systems were designed to give a ride as comfortable as a private car. The Routemaster was so reliable that some remained in daily use for nearly half a century, and many operational models still exist today. The second prototype RM2 is also in the collection and has been returned to its 1957 appearance, when it first entered passenger service.

1989/119

1998/86785

NS type motor bus, 1926

The earliest NS type buses, which entered service in 1923, had no roof, open cabs, and solid tyres (bottom left). Later types were designed with a covered top deck (bottom right) but still had solid tyres and open cabs. The NS had a 'dropped frame' chassis which was closer to the ground than previous buses, giving it a much lower centre of gravity and reduced risk of tipping, despite the increased weight on top. Its lower rear platform also made it much easier for passengers to get on and off. The improved design led to the bus being called the NS or 'no step' type, although some claimed it stood for 'nulli secundus', meaning 'second to none' in Latin. Our 1926 NS1995 (right) has been fitted with pneumatic (air-filled) tyres, and an enclosed cab, new features which were added in the late 1920s.

1981/516

 Interior fittings from this type of bus and many others can be found in the Small object store.

1981/516

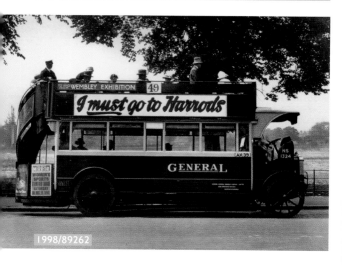

1998/89262

1998/75965

1986/8

DMS type bus, 1971

Since the late 1960s, buses have been designed to allow driver-only operation without a conductor. This meant the traditional layout of a double-decker had to be reversed. The entrance was positioned at the front, so passengers could pay as they got on, and the engine was relocated at the rear. After 1970 London Transport no longer designed its own buses; instead it bought cheaper but less robust 'off the peg' models from manufacturers. Our Daimler Fleetline DMS1 was the first of these standard bus types introduced in 1971. It was launched as the 'Londoner' but the name never caught on and was quickly dropped.

1986/8

2004/16203

1998/44748

Cycle Hire bike

The Transport for London Cycle Hire scheme went live on 30 July 2010 with 315 docking stations and 5,000 bikes. More than 12,000 members signed up to use the scheme and over 6,000 keys were activated. It operates 24 hours a day across a large area of central, east and southwest London. Over 36.5 million cycle hires have been completed since the scheme started. This bike at the Depot is one of two in the Museum's collection. The first bike, numbered 00001, is on display at Covent Garden.

Q1 type trolleybus, 1948

Soon after London Transport (LT) was created in 1933, a full tram to trolleybus conversion scheme began. By 1940, when the programme was interrupted by the Second World War, more than half of London's huge tram network had been replaced by trackless trolleybuses. Number 1768 is one of the final batch of large 70-seat vehicles built after the war to replace the A1 type 'Diddlers' and other vehicles destroyed in enemy bombing. It represents the final stage of trolleybus development in London. In 1962, only 10 years after replacing the trams in London, the trolleybus system was itself dismantled in favour of diesel buses. Most of the Q1 class were sold for further use in Spain.

Cycle hire bike

I'm a big advocate of cycling in the city: it's healthy and fun and helps reduce congestion. Therefore, my favourite object in the collection has to be the Cycle Hire bicycle. The cycle hire scheme is fantastic for people like me who don't have room to keep a bike in their house. I can still get out and experience amazing parts of my city by bike that I might otherwise miss. Recently, my partner and I set ourselves a challenge: to see how many bike-docking stations we could visit in one day. We travelled all over London, riding past famous landmarks and down quirky backstreets, and had a wonderful time. There's nothing quite like flying past the Houses of Parliament on a bike!

Vicki Pipe, Family and Community Programme Manager London Transport Museum

1982/30

 Green Line coaches and their routes feature in many of the designs in the Museum's poster collection.

TF type Green Line coach, 1939

After its formation in 1933, the London General Omnibus Company's successor London Transport continued the LGOC's practice of experimenting with new bus and coach designs at the Chiswick Works. The TF type was a very advanced vehicle in its day and the first London bus to be fitted with an underfloor engine allowing more space for seats. It has a stylish, streamlined body shape, with the radiator cap at the front built into an LT roundel (above right). The TF coach was designed for use on the newly developed Green Line express services to country towns outside London such as Windsor in Berkshire or Hitchin in Hertfordshire. When the Second World War broke out just weeks after the TF buses were introduced, they were converted into ambulances, only returning to service use after the war in 1946.

1982/30

1998/44392

The collection at the Depot includes an intriguing range of engineering material and equipment that has helped to power and control the city's transport and keep London on the move. You can explore more examples in the Engineering collection on our website.

At the Depot, the objects range from bus engines and lift motors to a tunnel ventilation fan and heavy electrical switch gear. Most of these are tried and tested machines which were in daily use for many years. There are also some fascinating experiments like the remnants of a spiral elevator found abandoned deep in a Piccadilly line Tube station.

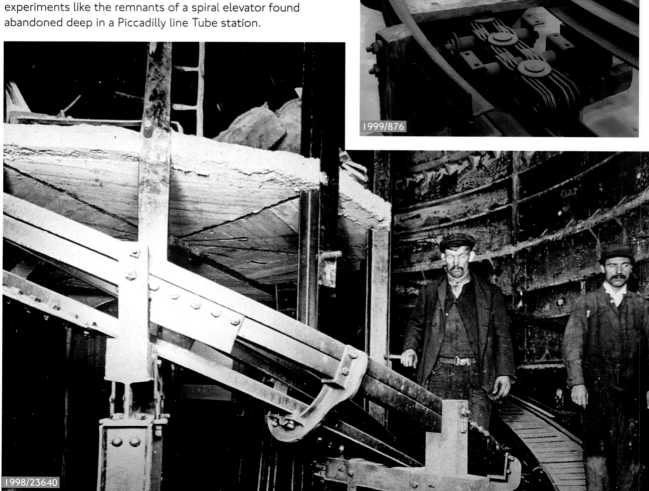

1999/876

1998/23640

Spiral elevator, 1906

When the first deep Tube line, City & South London Railway (C&SLR), opened in 1890 a reliable escalator had not yet been developed. This experimental moving walkway was installed in a spare lift shaft at Holloway Road station in 1906. It was built by Jesse Reno, the American inventor of the first working escalator, and William Henry Aston, patent holder for this spiral 'elevator'. Unfortunately, the spiral elevator was not a success and never operated in public service. Nearly a century later in 1993, its remains were found at the bottom of the lift shaft and brought to the Museum, and we have restored a four metre section of walkway. As it has no steps it cannot be called an 'escalator'. The first successful escalator on the Tube was installed at Earl's Court station in 1911.

1999/876

1993/5

Spiral elevator, 1906

Once a term, the Acton Depot is taken over by secondary school pupils to learn about careers in engineering. Students have a chance to explore the collection and discover the story of Transport for London's engineering wonders, such as the 1906 spiral elevator. Sadly, it was never used for public service. Although no official reason was given for abandoning this equipment, perhaps the narrow walkways, noise and lack of handrails meant that elegant Edwardian Londoners simply did not feel comfortable using it. Engineers went back to the drawing board and soon came up with a more efficient solution for transporting people safely in tight underground spaces, resulting in the escalators still used today. This is a great lesson for our students – that engineering isn't necessarily about finding the right answer straight away, but it can be a process of perseverance, trial and error and thinking creatively.

Liz Poulter, Inspire Engineering Officer London Transport Museum

Westinghouse power lever frame, c1906

Early railway signals and points were operated by large levers in signal boxes, connected by rods and wires to the equipment out on the ground. It was physically demanding work for the signalmen and the levers took up a lot of space. The new Tube railways built in the 1900s introduced colour light signalling and electro-pneumatic points which could be controlled from compact power lever frames, such as this one manufactured by Westinghouse, which was at York Road station, now closed. The technical advance meant less space was needed for equipment and a lot less physical effort from the signalmen. The frame has an illuminated diagram showing the position of a train passing through this section of track. The wooden cabinet houses the mechanical interlocking gear that prevents points and signals being set in dangerous combinations.

1993/5

BESI (Bus Electronic Scanning Indicator) equipment, 1957

The key to managing a regular bus service is knowing where each bus is located. A bus control system known as BESI was developed by London Transport in 1957. Roadside beacons, like the one on the right in the photo below, were installed at intervals along eight bus routes to collect information on the flow of buses. Buses were fitted with unique barcodes (bottom right) known as running plates. You can see one fitted to the left of the Air France advert on the bus in the photo. A light beam from the beacon scanner-head on the pavement was reflected from the running plate on each bus as it passed, recording its location. An electronic display panel on equipment (right) in a central control room showed the movement of buses along each route. Controllers could monitor the progress of each bus and contact inspectors along the route, who were able to make adjustments to the service to keep it regular.

1993/103, 1993/105, 1992/391

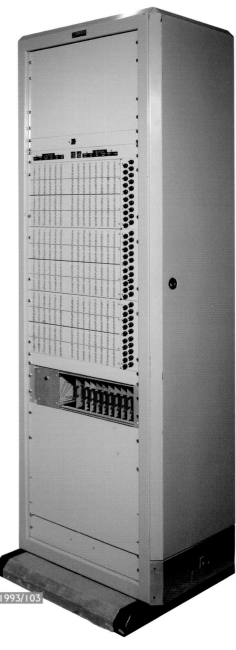

1993/103

1992/391

1993/105

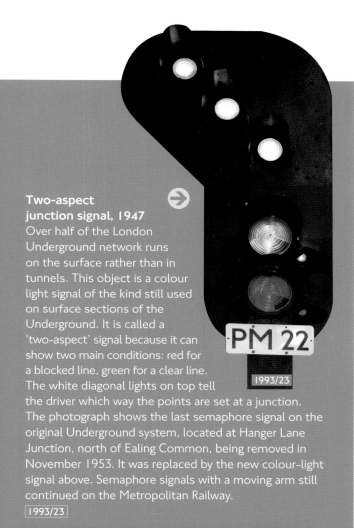

Two-aspect junction signal, 1947

Over half of the London Underground network runs on the surface rather than in tunnels. This object is a colour light signal of the kind still used on surface sections of the Underground. It is called a 'two-aspect' signal because it can show two main conditions: red for a blocked line, green for a clear line. The white diagonal lights on top tell the driver which way the points are set at a junction. The photograph shows the last semaphore signal on the original Underground system, located at Hanger Lane Junction, north of Ealing Common, being removed in November 1953. It was replaced by the new colour-light signal above. Semaphore signals with a moving arm still continued on the Metropolitan Railway.

1993/23

Public address machine, 1935

The lifts at Earl's Court station were the first to have automatic operation rather than an attendant. In 1935 this public address machine was installed at the station to warn passengers to 'stand clear of the gates' of the lift before they closed. The message was recorded on the soundtrack of a short piece of 35mm film mounted on a turntable inside a box. An optical pick-up inside the box converted the message into an electrical signal, which in turn was amplified and played through public address speakers. The machine talked to passengers for nearly 50 years before being decommissioned in 1984. Today all recorded messages broadcast on the Underground use digital technology.

1996/5442

1998/47685

1996/5442

1998/81079

Substation control panel, 1932

This panel was used until 2005 to control the supply of electricity from Manor House sub-station on the Piccadilly line. The direct current (DC) system used on the London Underground requires thick cables and short distances between sub-stations because of the high currents involved. By linking the operation of several sub-stations to a central control room, one person could manage the distribution of electricity over a greater area. When the Piccadilly line was extended north of Finsbury Park in 1932, all the new sub-stations were managed from one control room at Wood Green, including this panel linked down the line to Manor House.

2010/5042

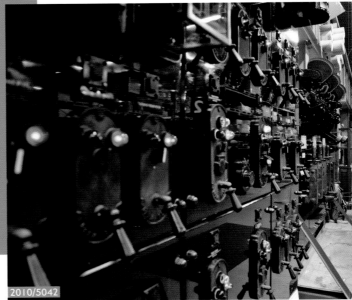

2010/5042

1999/39090

Underground line controller's desk, 1939

With so many trains moving so many passengers, some delays and cancellations are always a possibility on the Underground. To minimise disruption, each train is constantly monitored, with alterations made when problems arise. For many years, this desk from the control room based at Leicester Square was the focal point for managing daily events on the Central line. The telephone switchboard enabled communication with stations and signal cabins along the line. The system was installed in 1939 and replaced when the operation of the line was upgraded in 1979.

1999/39090

1998/48576

Hampstead Tube lift, 1907

The Hampstead Tube (now part of the Northern line) opened in 1907. Most of the stations had electric lifts installed by the American Otis Elevator Company. They were all produced to the same standard and size, with art nouveau floral decoration applied to the wooden doors and metal ventilation grilles. There were two lift cars in each circular shaft. If one got stuck, the adjacent lift could be stopped alongside and passengers transferred between cars through connecting doors. Our lift car is from Hampstead station, currently the deepest station on the London Underground system. This equipment was in use for over 80 years before it was replaced.

1982/64

1982/64

1999/8013

Hampstead Tube lift, 1907

When I travel by public transport I really enjoy spotting the features that denote London Underground's magnificent design history. This ventilation grille from the lift door at Hampstead station is an example of Leslie Green's distinctive Art Nouveau design. Although purely functional, disguising a ventilation hole in the lift door, Green still considered it worthy of attention and decorated it with stylised acanthus leaves. Details like this enhanced the interior of the stations and made travelling in London more interesting.

Valia Lamprou, Curatorial Assistant London Transport Museum

Escalator motor, 1939

Escalators can carry a continuous flow of passengers, so are far more efficient for moving large numbers of people than lifts. After the first escalators were installed at Earl's Court in 1911, they were routinely installed in new and existing Tube stations as the number of passengers increased during the 1920s and 30s. This electric motor, built by Laurence Scott & Electromotors Ltd, powered an escalator at Marylebone station from 1939 to 1996 when it was replaced.

1996/3250

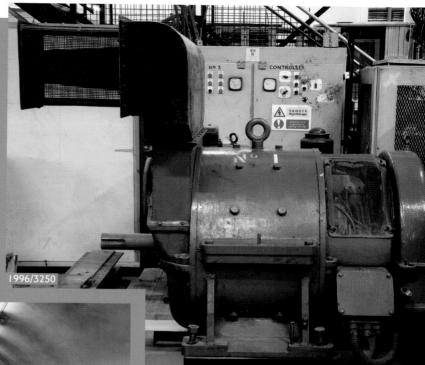

1996/3250

1998/67434

Gardner 6LXB diesel engine, 1970

The Gardner 6LXB diesel engine was used in the Daimler Fleetline DMS type bus introduced in 1971. This was the first standard rear engine double deck bus design purchased by London Transport.
The 10.4 litre diesel engine was more powerful than any previously fitted to a London bus and, unlike previous bus engines, it was mounted across the rear which made it easier to access for maintenance.

1988/56

In the photograph collection, you can see Helen Clifford, London Transport's first female bus engineer, working on a similar engine in 1986.

1988/56

1981/534

Class 6A tramcar truck, 1930

This tramcar truck was designed for use on trams serving routes with hills. It contained two electric traction motors to help the tram safely climb steep gradients. In the event of a power failure a run-back brake would automatically operate, stopping the tram from running down the hill. It was fitted to class HR/2 trams (right) operated by London County Council Tramways (LCCT). The HR stood for 'hilly route'.

LCCT operated many tram lines in central and south London before being taken over by London Transport in 1933. The first section of electric tramway was opened by the Prince of Wales on 15 May 1903 and ran from Westminster Bridge to Tooting.

1981/534

1998/88421

1998/74901

1994/11

Mercury arc rectifier, 1920

Electricity is generated by power stations in the form of high voltage alternating current (AC), but Underground trains use a Direct Current (DC) system for motive power. The AC supply from London Underground's main power station at Lots Road was converted to DC at trackside sub-stations around the network using machines called mercury arc rectifiers. This one, manufactured by British Thomson-Houston, was installed at Old Oak Common in west London to provide power for the overground extension of the Central line to Ealing Broadway in 1920. It is mounted on insulated struts and would have had safety barriers all around it because the exterior steel tank filled with mercury was 'live' with electricity when in use.

1994/11

2014/3508

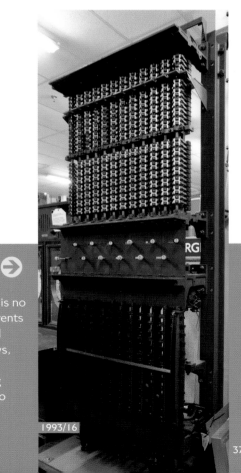

RG

1993/16

Interlocking machine, 1957

This machine replaced the lever frames used by signalmen on the Underground since the early 1900s. Its function is to ensure that there is no conflict between the routes set by the points and the signals. This prevents collisions between trains that might otherwise accidentally be signalled to use the same section of track. The levers on the front move sideways, instead of backwards and forwards like a hand-operated signal frame. They are moved by compressed air controlled by a signalman operating a push-button panel. If the air supply failed, the signalman could go into the Interlocking Machine Room and operate the levers manually.

1993/16

1998/86262

The Museum has many objects which help to show how the infrastructure of London Transport has evolved. These range from mocked-up designs and models of stations to actual architectural and decorative features saved from transport locations across London during modernisation. You can see a selection of the best examples of design in the Design gallery in our online museum.

Some models show schemes proposed by architects and designers before they went ahead, others were for public display to showcase the latest developments at the time. Often they are a valuable record of infrastructure which has since been replaced and has now disappeared.

1994/207

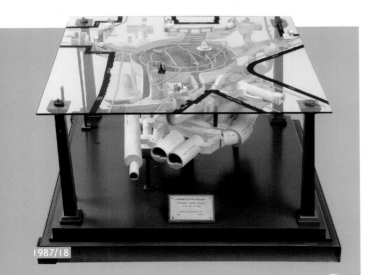

1987/18

Piccadilly Circus station reconstruction model, c1927

This model was built by a young engineer called Harold Harding working on a huge four-year Underground reconstruction project. Harding and his wife made the model at home out of cardboard to show the complexity of the scheme in three dimensions. The Piccadilly Circus project was completed in 1928. Harding went on to become one of the country's leading civil engineers and was knighted for his achievements.

1987/18

Underground booking office window surround, 1906

This is a typical feature from one of more than 40 stations designed by architect Leslie Green for the three Underground railways opened in 1906-07, the Bakerloo, Piccadilly and Hampstead Tubes. It is made of glazed ceramic blocks called faience, the same material used on the exterior of the station buildings. The entrance hall interiors were all decorated in green tiling with the exteriors in dark red. Most of these windows have been replaced since the 1980s but some stations have been renovated with replicas of these art nouveau originals.

1994/207

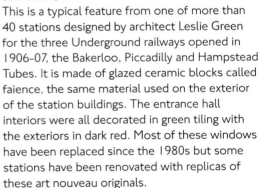

1998/88056

2010/2832

1982/12

Time recording clock, 1924

From the very earliest days in the 1830s, timekeepers monitored the bus services in London. In the early twentieth century bus services were overseen by inspectors stationed along a route, who could check timings and adjust the service by getting drivers to turn around before the terminus. This was an expensive and inefficient use of staff resources outside the busy central area. To solve this problem, some 250 time recording clocks like this were installed at bus stations and turning points in suburban and country areas. On arrival, the bus conductor inserted a special log card which was stamped with the place, date and time to provide a record of the service for checking. The introduction of one person operation and difficulties over maintaining the clocks led to their withdrawal. The last ones were taken out of service in 1972.

1982/12

Underground ticket machine, 1937

London Underground first introduced coin-operated ticket machines in the 1920s, long before they were used on the other railways. Early machines could accept any combination of coins, but could not give change. This improved model, manufactured by Brecknell, Munro & Rogers, was able to dispense change, and became the standard machine until the 1980s. The blue 'tombstone' casing with an illuminated, angled face is a classic design by architect Charles Holden.

2010/2832

1998/63472

1998/64870

2000/10191

2004/15120

Canary Wharf station entrance model, c1993

The stations of the Jubilee Line Extension, opened in 1999, feature the most impressive Underground architecture since Charles Holden's work on the Piccadilly and Northern lines in the 1930s. This is the presentation model by Norman Foster Associates for the entrance to Canary Wharf station – the most spacious Tube station in London. It features a dramatic glazed roof over the main escalators to the large booking hall. The station was contained within a reinforced concrete box built below the former West India Dock.

2000/10191

2014/9346

1995/51

Tiled Way Out sign from Green Park station platform, 1906

At platform level the Bakerloo, Piccadilly and Hampstead Tubes were decorated in different coloured tile patterns to give each station an individual identity. It was one of the biggest tiling jobs ever carried out in London. This restored detail with the 'Way Out' lettering fired into the tiles was removed from Green Park. Since 1990, modernisation has meant most original tiles have been replaced but at some London Underground stations, like Covent Garden (see photo above) the original patterns and features have been carefully replicated.

1995/51

2010/23075

Memorial panels from Manor House Hospital laboratory, Golders Green c1950

These sculpted panels were on the facade of a medical research laboratory at Manor House hospital which was paid for by donations from London bus workers, to commemorate colleagues killed or injured in the Second World War. They were saved when the laboratory building was demolished in the 1990s. The right hand panel is probably the only sculpted image of a London Transport trolleybus in existence.

2000/15806

Memorial to George Shave, 1933

This is an elaborate memorial to George Shave, chief engineer of the LGOC from 1917-33. Shave created and managed the bus engineering works at Chiswick in the 1920s, where mass production procedures adopted from American factories revolutionised bus engineering development and maintenance in London. The memorial was paid for by staff subscription at Chiswick and displayed in the main offices of the works after Shave's death in 1933.

2010/23075

1998/83971

2000/15806

Section model of Bank Waterloo & City line station and Trav-o-lator c1960

Trav-o-lators are mechanically similar to escalators, but without steps, and are used to speed up passenger traffic through tunnel walkways. This was the first Trav-o-lator in Britain, installed in 1959 adjacent to the Waterloo & City line platforms at Bank station. This short Tube shuttle line was operated by the mainline railway and has never had a rail link to the rest of the Underground system. It was only transferred from British Rail to London Underground operation in 1993, when the original Southern Railway trains built in 1940 were replaced. The model shows the trains in their green Southern Region 1960s livery (see photo, bottom left).

1992/394

1992/394

Trolleybus feeder pillar

Feeder pillars were an important part of the overhead electricity supply of the trolleybus system. They were positioned at half mile sections along the route to switch off the power for maintenance or repairs. This example has a compartment for a staff telephone. The shape of these pillars reflected contemporary industrial design by Adams, Holden & Pearson.

I remember seeing these pillars beside traction poles with the feeder wires going up to the overhead but I never got to see a box open and the switchgear inside. Most work was done at night unless there was a service failure that a tower wagon would attend.

Bob Bird, Senior Curator
London Transport Museum

1995/247

2009/8121

LGOC Chiswick Works gates, 1921

These ornamental wrought iron gates stood on Chiswick High Road, west London, at the main entrance to the London General Omnibus Company's (LGOC) giant centralised bus works, opened in 1921. In 1933 London Transport took over this facility for the construction, repair and regular overhaul of the world's largest bus fleet. Chiswick also housed experimental and training facilities including a skid pan, an area used to test buses' handling. Around 3,000 staff walked through these gates every working day. The home of London bus engineering was closed and demolished in 1990 as buses were bought from external manufacturers and maintained locally at bus garages by private operators.

1999/2262

1999/2262

London County Council Tramways (LCCT) passenger shelter, c1920

This large wooden passenger shelter, located outside the Depot, is believed to have originally been sited on the LCC tramway system somewhere in south London. The shelter was moved by London Transport in 1947 to a busy stop on its country bus network at Redhill Hospital in Surrey as seen in this photograph. The site was redeveloped in 1995 and the decaying shelter was brought back to London for preservation. We have renovated it and restored the original wooden shingled roof.

1995/2159

 The shelter now has a third life accommodating passengers waiting to ride the Acton Miniature Railway at the Depot on Open Weekends.

1998/62447

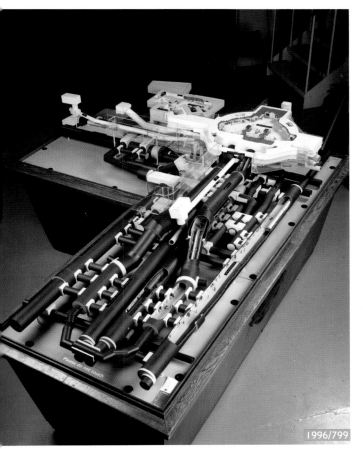

1996/799

Oxford Circus station model, c1965

This large and detailed official model was built to show the planned reconstruction of Oxford Circus station when the building of the Victoria line was underway. The new Tube line crossed the existing Central and Bakerloo lines at this station and a single new booking hall and passenger interchange between all three was needed. The model shows 1959 stock in the new station tunnels (see below) suggesting that it was built before the design of the new Victoria line trains was finalised.

1996/799

Horology collection

I've always been interested in the history of time, and was delighted to discover the Museum's little-known collection of clocks and time-keepers. Railways played a crucial role in the introduction of standardised time during the nineteenth century, as it was necessary to ensure that trains all ran to the same time. This was especially important for the safety of trains due to run in opposite directions on sections of single track. Along with the timetables, this collection demonstrates how our society has become ever more preoccupied with measuring and managing time.

Maria Blyzinsky, Curator of Astronomy Royal Observatory Greenwich, 1992-99

Signage on the early twentieth century Underground was confusing and inconsistent. It was a product of earlier times when the lines belonged to separate railway companies.

Nothing was standardised so it was difficult for passengers to find their way or know where they were. As Commercial Officer for the Underground Group in the early 1900s, Frank Pick was committed to making the travel environment more attractive and passenger journeys easier. Clear signage and easy-to-follow maps were an important part of this. Our large collection of enamel signs and maps shows how the Underground and London Transport led the way in helping travellers to navigate the city. As the transport system became busier and more complex, visual travel aids had to become simpler to remain effective.

PASSENGERS TO LONDON TRAVEL DIRECT TO EUSTON JOINING THE METROPOLITAN RAILWAY AT EUSTON SQUARE STATION ELECTRIC TRAINS TO ALL PARTS.

32. WESTBOURNE TERRACE. 1910.

R.H. SELBIE. General Manager

1992/387

Metropolitan Railway enamel sign, 1910
An example of competitive advertising, this sign promoting the Metropolitan Railway's services would have been placed at a station on the mainline railway out of Euston, such as Watford Junction. It makes no mention of the rival Tube connections available to passengers travelling into London beyond Euston. Robert Selbie, the newly appointed General Manager of the Metropolitan Railway at this time, was determined to keep his company independent of the Underground Group. There was very little joint promotion between them, and Selbie rejected all proposals for a merger. However, both were eventually absorbed into London Transport in 1933.

1992/387

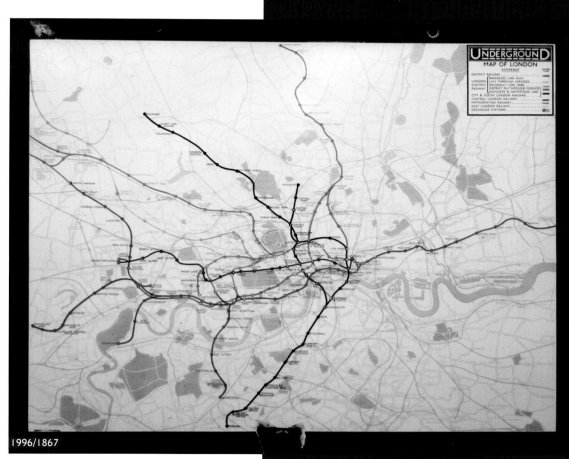

1996/1867

1998/51631

Enamel Underground map of London, 1933

This map in enamelled steel shows a geographical representation of London and its Underground services, including the new Piccadilly line extension to Cockfosters which can be seen at the top. It shows the limitations of using a geographical layout, where the outer stations of the Metropolitan and District lines are beyond the edge of the map. Large enamel maps like this were phased out in the 1930s and replaced with paper poster maps which were easier to update. The new poster maps with Henry Beck's ingenious diagram (see page 48) gave the whole system a more balanced appearance.

1996/1867

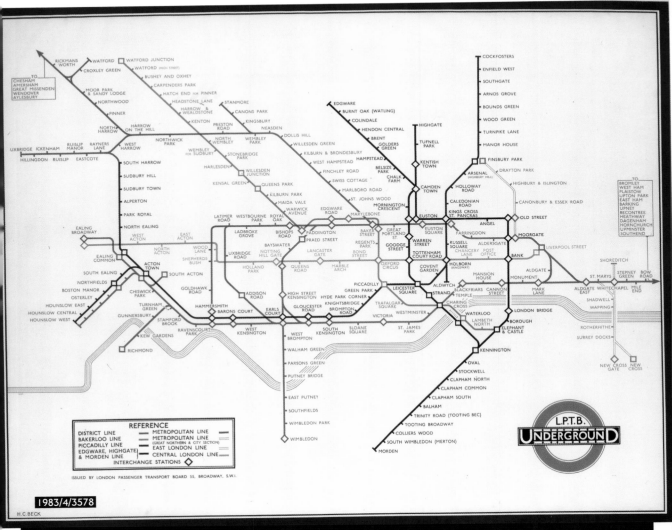

1983/4/3578

H.C. BECK

1998/57799

Underground poster map, 1933

Henry Beck revolutionised the Tube map by redesigning it as a diagram. This is the first poster-size version printed by the Underground in 1933, a few months after the success of his first pocket map. Beck enlarged the central area in relation to the outer area, with all the stations the same distance apart. Each colour coded line is shown as a precise horizontal, vertical or 45° diagonal. In his design, Beck abandoned geographical accuracy but made the map much easier to use. London Underground has applied the principles of his design system ever since and it has been adopted by transport networks across the globe.

1983/4/3578

1998/1514

Frank Pick's office furniture, c1930

Frank Pick rose from the position of Commercial Officer to become Managing Director of the Underground in the 1920s. Under his guidance, a culture of good design and 'fitness for purpose' was applied across the organisation. It became one of the defining characteristics of London Transport. Pick's selection of the best-designed furniture for 55 Broadway, the new Underground headquarters building at St James's Park completed in 1929, show his principles working on a personal level. Practical, well designed items throughout our Depot demonstrate his determination that 'London Transport is or will be a work of art'.

1998/1514

Examples of artwork commissioned by Pick for London Transport in the 1920s and 30s can be seen in the Posters and artwork collection.

Lego Underground map, 2013

It is hard to imagine London without the Tube map. The current version is a distant relative of the first, published back in 1908. One of the most unusual maps in the collection is made entirely of LEGO bricks. In 2013 five different LEGO replicas were built to celebrate 150 years of London Underground, each one representing a different era. I went along to Green Park station to see the 1968 map on display. It had attracted a large crowd of foreign tourists and they were struggling to navigate using the LEGO replica, which was 45 years out of date. Once reconnected with the current Tube map they headed off in the right direction.

Caroline MacVay, Curator
London Transport Museum

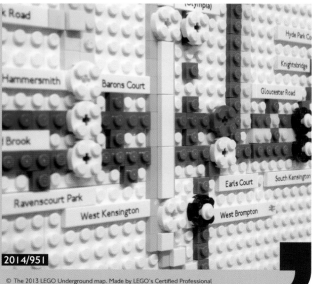

2014/951

© The 2013 LEGO Underground map. Made by LEGO's Certified Professional Duncan Titmarsh, with kind permission of The LEGO Group.

Cabinet with complete set of Johnston letterface wooden printing blocks, c1920

In 1913, expert calligrapher Edward Johnston was commissioned by Frank Pick to design a new display typeface for the exclusive use of the Underground Group. He delivered the first version of his classic design in 1916. This cabinet of wooden printing blocks was used for decades by printers to produce the text and captions for Underground posters and signs. An amended version of the typeface called New Johnston was developed by Eiichi Kono in 1980 for a wider range of uses in smaller documents such as timetables and leaflets. It remains Transport for London's standard and exclusive typeface today.

1985/56

1985/56

Johnston letterface wooden printing blocks, c1920

My absolute favourite objects in the collection are the Johnston Font printing blocks. The Johnston Font, so celebrated for its use on London's transport system since 1916, is a wonderful typeface. It is elegant and clean with unique characteristics instantly recognisable, even to children. The blocks are well crafted – it is clear that they were painstakingly created. It was a time when print was a real craft, somewhat lost in today's digital world. The font is dynamic and has been slightly adapted over time, with Percy Delf Smith creating a 'petit-serif' version in the 1920s and Eric Gill who took inspiration from the Johnston typeface to produce his own celebrated Gill Sans design. Today Transport for London uses another variation, called New Johnston designed by Eiichi Kono. Being able to handle the original blocks provides a tangible understanding of why this font is so special.

Sau-Fun Mo, Head of Design
London Transport Museum

Hillingdon (Swakeleys) station name-boards, c1935

We have two of these framed name-boards rescued from the old Underground station at Hillingdon in west London before it was demolished to make way for the A40(M) motorway in the early 1990s. The station was opened by the Metropolitan Railway on its Uxbridge branch in 1923. These 'tombstone-style' name-boards with the Underground's 'bar and circle' are a 1920s design but were only put up at Hillingdon after London Transport took over from the Metropolitan Railway in the 1930s. A completely new replacement station for Hillingdon – with 'Swakeleys' dropped from the title – opened nearby in 1994.

`1994/673`

1994/673

Tufnell Park Underground station nameplate, c1908

This 'bar and disc' nameplate marks the first step in the evolution of the Underground's famous roundel device, which has become a symbol of London. Distinctive platform name-boards, with white lettering on a blue bar across a red enamel disc, were introduced in 1908. A complete set of original name-boards for Tufnell Park station was discovered in a store at the station decades after they had been replaced by more modern versions.

`1998/6013`

1998/6013

Leicester Square station name-board, 1935

The Underground's original 'bar and disc' symbol had evolved into the 'bar and circle' by the 1920s. Managing Director Frank Pick asked the calligrapher Edward Johnston to redesign the symbol to include his new lettering. The new design was known as the 'bull's-eye' and was adopted by London Transport in 1933. Architect Charles Holden introduced bronze-framed silhouette signs like this for new and reconstructed stations such as Leicester Square, which was rebuilt in 1935. The term 'roundel' officially replaced the 'bull's-eye' name in 1972 following an internal design review.

`1996/5533`

1996/5533

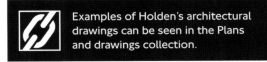

Examples of Holden's architectural drawings can be seen in the Plans and drawings collection.

Our small object store has a controlled environment, giving the best conditions for preserving hundreds of small delicate items, which are kept in metal drawers and glass-fronted cases. There is no particular theme to this material other than their size and, in some cases, fragility.

This store room includes toys and models of vehicles and equipment and items reflecting the experience of staff and passengers running and riding the system over almost two hundred years. Everything in our collection has been preserved because of its significance in representing some aspect of the rich story that links people, transport and the development of London.

1998/87163

1994/837

London Transport bus inspector's cap badge, c1980

As well as the familiar bar and circle 'bull's-eye' symbol known today as the roundel, London Transport adopted an image of the mythical griffin as a heraldic device in 1933. The griffin has the body of a lion and the head and wings of an eagle and symbolises wisdom and strength. The bull's-eye and the griffin were combined together in the cap badges worn by senior uniformed staff on the road and rail services. The design remained unchanged for 50 years, up to the 1980s. The example above is a London Transport bus inspector's cap badge.

1994/837

London Transport Gibson roll ticket machine, 1953

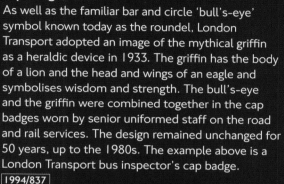

1994/1197

Until the 1950s, the conductor's rack of brightly coloured pre-printed tickets and the 'ting' of the cancelling bell punch was a feature of every bus journey. From 1953 London Transport (LT) introduced a new roll ticket machine invented by George Gibson, superintendent of the LT ticket punch works in Brixton. It was used for 40 years on London buses. The Gibson machine carried a roll of blank paper inside and the conductor could set the machine's dials to print and issue a ticket of any value.

1994/1197

1998/20119

2019/1023

Ride With Pride badge, 2018

These unofficial badges were handed out informally to TfL staff. They feature the campaign slogan 'Ride With Pride' championed by TfL's LGBT+ staff network group OUTbound. One of several staff networks groups, OUTbound works to provide a safe and inclusive work environment for LGBT+ colleagues. It runs campaigns and regularly has a presence at London Pride events.

2019/1023

1983/211

London Transport bus stop flag, 1935

The first experimental bus stops were installed by the London General Omnibus Company in 1913. They started to appear in larger numbers after the First World War, but it was not until 1935 that a comprehensive scheme of fixed bus stops along a whole route was introduced. The sign itself is called a 'flag', and this example was used in London Transport's country bus area in Kent at a stop shared with Maidstone and District services.

1983/211

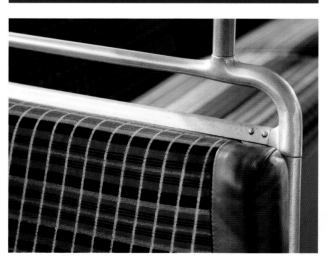

2001/5251

Moquette

Moquette is the hardwearing woollen fabric that has been used to cover seats on all London buses and Underground trains since the 1920s. It has never been replaced by metal or plastic seating as in many other cities' transport systems. Since 1936 noted textile designers have been commissioned to produce new moquette patterns. Our collection of samples goes back to the 1920s and comes right up to date, including the 2012 designs by Heatherwick Studio for the seats of the New Routemaster bus.

1995/522, 1996/577, 1995/518

1995/522

1996/577

1995/518

 You will see many examples of the different types of moquette in our road and rail vehicle collections.

2006/7594

Sherlock Holmes tiles from Baker Street station, 1979

Baker Street station was partly rebuilt and completely refurbished when the first stage of the Jubilee line was opened in 1979. The decorative theme was based on the famous but fictional detective who lived at 221B Baker Street. The tiles were used throughout the modernised areas, including these specially designed tiles featuring Sherlock Holmes' distinctive profile. In Sir Arthur Conan Doyle's stories, first published in 1887, the characters of Holmes and his assistant Dr Watson occasionally travelled by Underground.

1987/64

1987/64

1983/301/3

1998/85795

British Transport Commission Police helmet, c1948

London Transport (LT) established its own police force in 1933. When transport was nationalised in 1948, LT's police force came under the control of the British Transport Commission (BTC), although it remained a separate entity with its own Chief of Police. The BTC was abolished in 1963 but the police force continued as a special national force, renamed the British Transport Police (BTP). This helmet dates from around 1948 and the badge features a griffin – one of London Transport's symbols.

1983/411/1

CHRISTMAS PUDDING

Directions : Remove the paper and place the pudding in a basin. Steam or boil for 1½ hours taking care that no water gets into the pudding.

INGREDIENTS :
VINE FRUITS
MIXED PEEL
SUET
BREADCRUMBS
SUGAR

4/6

FLOUR
EGGS
ALMONDS
CARROTS
LEMONS
SPICES

2lbs net.

2012/55357

1997/1978

London Transport Catering products, c1970

The griffin was also used as the symbol of London Transport Catering, which provided meals and refreshments to staff at every canteen and depot. Staff could buy some of the products for use at home, and the strong Griffin tea and Christmas puddings, made at LT's Food Production Centre at Croydon, were particularly popular.

2012/55357, 1997/1978

Greenwich Heritage Centre collection

Ship's bell from Woolwich Ferry Boat John Benn, 1930

This brass ship's bell (located in area 4 under the mezzanine) is from one of the London County Council (LCC) paddle steamers, which worked on the free vehicle ferry service across the Thames at Woolwich between 1930 and 1965. The John Benn was named after one of the original members of the London County Council elected in 1888, who became LCC Chairman in 1904. When the paddle steamer was withdrawn, the ship's bell was saved and mounted on a stand. The Woolwich ferry service is now operated by TfL's London River Services using modern diesel-powered vessels.
2013/2129

2013/2129

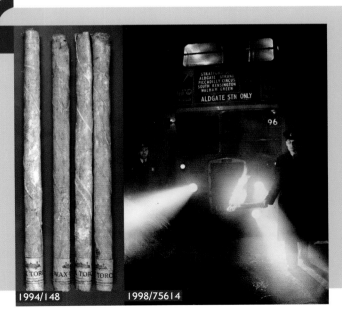

1994/148   1998/75614

Fog flare

During the notoriously thick London smogs of the 1950s, bright flares were often carried by bus conductors walking in front of the bus to guide the driver along. The fog flares in our collection remind me of a story my mother once told. My parents lived in Mitcham and they frequently drove to Buckinghamshire to visit my mother's parents. One foggy day, they got lost somewhere along the Edgware Road. My mother got out to try to find out where they were. She took a few steps to look around — but the fog was so thick that she lost sight of my father's van. My father had to guide her back to safety by calling out.

Robert Excell, Curator
London Transport Museum

1996/3495

1996/4192

Moulded ceramic tiles by Harold Stabler, c1938

In the late 1930s Harold Stabler, one of the partners at Poole Pottery in Dorset, was commissioned to produce a series of moulded tile designs to decorate new and reconstructed stations. The relief designs would add texture to the plain biscuit colour tiles used on platform walls. These examples from St. Paul's station show St. Paul's Cathedral and the London Transport headquarters at 55 Broadway, as well as the coats of arms of Middlesex and Buckinghamshire, both counties served by London Transport.

1996/3495, 1996/4192, 1996/3629, 1996/4169

1996/3629

1999/26870

London Transport silver medallion award for bravery, 1941

During the six years of the Second World War (1939-45), around 22,500 members of London Transport staff served in the Armed Forces, Merchant Navy, or Civil Defence. Nearly 700 of them were killed on active service. During air-raid attacks on London, 426 staff were killed and nearly 3,000 injured both on and off duty. In February 1941, after months of devastating aerial bombing during the Blitz, London Transport introduced this special medallion design. It was awarded for 'bravery and devotion to duty' to recognise some of the many individual acts of heroism by staff on the Home Front.

1999/26870

1996/4169

London United Electric Tramways (LUET) Challenge Cup for Cribbage, 1905

Most of the London bus, tram and Underground companies had their own staff social and sporting clubs, which continued under London Transport after 1933. We have a large collection of sports trophies, ranging from athletics and golf to cricket and football. Some were competitions between depots and there were even challenge cups for international contests such as rugby with the Paris Metro. This is the earliest example in the collection, an elaborate cup for the London United Electric Tramways inter-depot cribbage championship. It was first presented in 1906 by Lady Clifton Robinson, wife of the LUET managing director. It is engraved with winners' names right up to 1983, by which time all the former tram depots had long since become bus garages.

2003/9829

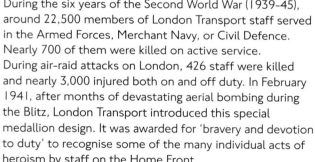

2003/9829

1998/42920

2014/1199

2014/1885

1995/2626

Bassett-Lowke Ashfield station model and Standard stock Tube cars, 1935

In 1934 London Transport (LT) exhibited a large working model railway layout in the booking hall of Charing Cross Underground station. It was built by the specialist engineering model-makers Bassett-Lowke and was such a popular attraction that the company soon added a working Tube train and a Charles Holden style station model to their sales catalogue. The station in the model was named Ashfield after the LT chairman, Lord Ashfield. These models were much more expensive to buy than those mass produced by Hornby, because they were scale models rather than toys.

2014/1199, 2014/1885

 This station model even includes miniature versions of historic posters. Some of the originals can be seen in the Museum's poster collection.

Advertisement for Hayward's Military Pickle, early 20th century

Our Small object store is a treasure trove of items able to evoke powerful memories of journeys made by association with larger settings. This advert transports me to a sunlit morning on board our NS type bus, steadily climbing the hill towards Crystal Palace on the annual London to Brighton Historic Commercial Vehicle Society run. It was the first time I had noticed the advert on the window and I remember chuckling at it as the sun streamed through the window illuminating it.

Chris Nix, Assistant Director, Collections and Engagement, London Transport Museum

The Library collection has around 15,000 items and represents a unique resource for the study of London's transport – past, present and future. The Library is located at Albany House in Petty France, not far from the Museum in Covent Garden. The reserve collection of lesser-used material is stored at the Depot, along with two special collections – Frank Pick's collection of personal papers and writings, and the Reinohl collection of bus tickets and related ephemera covering the earliest horse bus era up to the 1950s.

Apart from the Reinohl collection the Museum also has over 40,000 individual tickets from all forms of road and rail transport. One of the earliest examples is a pre-paid brass fare token made around 1862 for the horse tramway operated by American entrepreneur, George F Train.

We also have a large collection of maps, leaflets, booklets and other printed ephemera produced as information and publicity material by London's transport operators. The various companies and London Transport in particular from its formation in 1933, became increasingly adept at marketing and promotion. London Transport was responsible for providing vital services to nearly nine million people in the urban area and countryside around it. Because of the sheer scale and significance of the transport network, London Transport also found itself acting as the main visitor and information service for national events, such as the 1948 London Olympics, the Festival of Britain in 1951 and the Queen's Coronation celebrations in 1953. London Transport's successor, Transport for London, has continued in this role since its creation in 2000, notably managing the impact on London of the 2012 Olympics.

1986/69/4

1998/1851

1984/51/241

© Estate of Abram Games and Transport for London

Frank Pick collection

This collection holds the personal papers of Frank Pick (1878 –1941), London Transport's first Chief Executive, the man credited amongst other things with introducing the Underground's famous poster programme and transforming the Tube into 'London's longest art gallery'. Pick had a profound impact on the company and on London. Conceiving and commissioning a bold modernist image for London's transport network, Pick oversaw a golden age for design and architecture and his influence can still be clearly seen today in London and cities around the world. Dating from 1887 to Pick's death in 1941 the collection contains a wide range of material on subjects as diverse as love poetry, a living wage for London and comparative histories of London's traffic, many of them written in Pick's distinctive green ink. The papers reflect Pick's extraordinary energy and enthusiasm both in his roles within London's transport companies and his work as a founding member and later President of the Design and Industries Association and the first Chairman of the Council for Art and Industry.

Metro-land, 1924

The term 'Metro-land' was invented by the Metropolitan Railway's publicity department in 1915. It was a catchy name to promote the area in which it was developing both commuter housing and rail services north-west of London. It was one of the most successful suburban development promotions ever devised. Metro-land offered new houses near the countryside but also close to a station with a fast service to central London. The guide was produced every year to attract day trippers and especially home buyers. The 1924 edition features the new Wembley stadium on the cover and a full guide to the British Empire Exhibition, which put Wembley on the map. The guides were published annually until 1932, the year before the Metropolitan Railway was incorporated into the newly formed London Transport.

Pleasure outings, 1935

In the 1930s, at a time when few people owned a car, London Transport published booklets encouraging trips to the countryside around London by Green Line motor coach. Hiking and rambling were particularly popular and a long running series of Country Walks booklets was produced right up to the 1980s. This cover shows the lion cut into a chalk hillside on the North Downs to represent London Zoo's 'country branch' at Whipsnade, then a newly opened attraction.

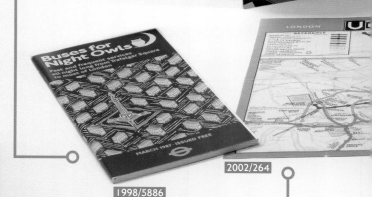

1995/625

Buses for Night Owls, 1987

A leaflet promoting the night bus services in London, which were expanded in the 1980s to meet growing demand both from clubbers and night shift workers. This cover is an early use of the New Johnston typeface designed in 1980, which is suitable for a range of fonts and sizes. Johnston's original 1916 font was only designed for use as a large display face for posters and signs. It was never used for books and leaflets.

You can see the original Johnston printing blocks in the Maps and signage collection.

1998/5886

2002/264

Pocket Underground map, 1908

This free pocket map issued by the Underground Group in 1908 is the first example of joint marketing, where the separate railway companies are shown together on one map. The company was at this time in a tough financial position as the new, expensively built deep Tube lines were not attracting enough passengers to pay back the investment of the Underground Group's shareholders. This clear, colour-coded map was a key item in the company's promotional strategy and it capitalised on travellers seeking to make their way to the hugely popular 1908 Franco British Exhibition, and London Olympics.

4/14991

1997/11047

2011/6768, 2011/6767, 2011/6762, 2011/6761

London Transport carried on, 1947
The official history of London Transport's war effort was written by journalist Charles Graves. It was published as a paperback with this striking cover only two years after the end of the Second World War. It is a surprisingly lively account for an official history, well-illustrated with LT official and press photographs, personal stories and just the right balance of Blitz spirit and propaganda.

Overground timetables, 2010
These are examples of the eye-catching timetable booklets produced by Transport for London in 2010. They commemorate the launch of the Overground inner suburban rail services which are linked to, but separate from, the Underground. For the first time since 1908, when a similar service known as the 'Outer Circle' ended, it is now quick and easy to get around the inner suburbs of London by rail without needing to travel through the city centre.

 Timetables such as these have been used since the earliest railways, alongside station clocks, which can be found throughout the Depot.

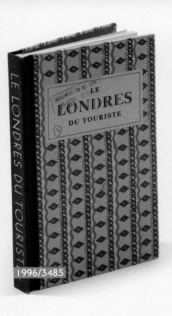

1996/3485

1997/11622

Visitor's London, 1954

Visitor's London, written by Harold Hutchison, Publicity Officer for London Transport, was promoted as 'an alphabetical reference book for the visitor to London who wishes also to see something of London's countryside'. It was also published in French as Le Londre du Touriste. As you would expect, all the journeys suggested are by bus and Underground. The cover designs are by painter and illustrator Edward Bawden for the Curwen Press. Inside, the guide is illustrated by ten well-known artists in all, including William Fenton, MacDonald Gill and Eric Ravilious.

1996/3485, 1997/11622

1996/7690

An Alphabet of TOT, illustrated by Charles Pears, 1915

This little book is a favourite of mine for a number of reasons. It was produced in 1915 to raise funds to support transport workers fighting in the First World War (TOT stands for: Train, Omnibus, Tram). It's a poignant reminder of a dark period in our history, but at the same time it's a charming, light-hearted way to help children learn the alphabet. Beautifully illustrated by Charles Pears, each letter tells part of the transport story. For M we have, 'M is for Map which will make every way, of the mighty Metropolis plain as the day'. Letter U tells us, 'U is the Underground, pride of the nation, the triumph of science and civilisation'. The artist captured a wealth of detail about London life in 1915 and even placed himself in the frame under letters V and Z. So, plenty for parents and children to talk about, and you can still buy the alphabet as a poster in our Museum shop today!

Caroline Warhurst,
Library and Information Services Manager
London Transport Museum

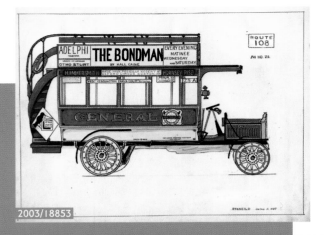

2003/18853

Reinohl collection

The Reinohl collection consists of 185 albums compiled by two brothers, Herbert and Albert Reinohl. The albums contain their personal collection of tickets, illustrations and press cuttings, relating mainly to early buses and trams in London. The collection represents a unique and invaluable research tool for those studying early road transport operations. Born in the late nineteenth century the brothers spent their boyhood years in London, where they began collecting tickets. Continuing this interest as adults they built a comprehensive record of the development of London's bus and tram services from the earliest days. Tickets offer an excellent primary source of information, particularly about little known suburban horse bus operators. The brothers must also have made detailed notes about the vehicles themselves as they turned their artistic talents to producing retrospectively about 180 watercolour drawings of horse and motor buses, showing route details, liveries and advertisements carried. The collection covers London bus services from 1829, and provincial and overseas services, through to the 1950s.

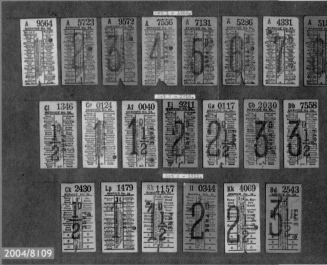

2004/8109

2003/2681

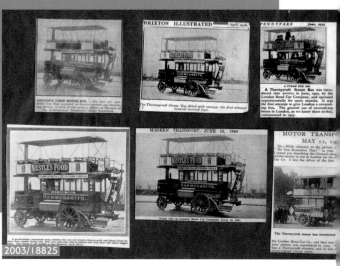

2003/18825

2011/1553

Metropolitan Railway third class workman's ticket, 1901

This workman's ticket was issued by the Metropolitan Railway in 1901. It is the return half of a third-class ticket from Westminster to Baker Street. The large 'O' overprinted in red means it was valid on the Outer Rail of the Circle Service. The Metropolitan Railway introduced cheap workmen's fares in May 1864. When the line was extended to Moorgate in December 1865, these became a statutory requirement. In 1901, for a cheap return fare of 3d (three old pennies), workmen were permitted to travel on trains before 7am, and could return after 12 noon by any train that day.

2011/1553

From your home by Underground and To the river by tram, postcards, 1913

Before the First World War, Londoners were taking more than twice as many journeys as they had done in 1900. Promotional publicity like this aimed to highlight the integrated nature of the growing transport systems in London. Electric trains and trams could carry people from new homes in the leafy suburbs to the river for leisure, or to work in a city office.

2007/2764

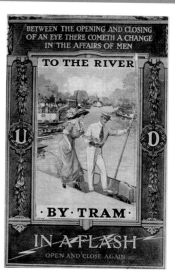

2007/2764

2005/2387

London Transport Magazine, 1967

We are lucky enough to have a full set of staff magazines at the Museum dating back to 1913. This copy of the London Transport Magazine dated May 1967 shows bus driver Tom Humfrey and conductor Lucy McCreary, both from West Ham bus garage, on the cover. The magazines are a fantastic resource for information about developments in London's transport and stories about the people that made them happen. In many cases the magazines may be the only record of someone having worked for the company, because personnel records often don't survive. So they are an important source for family history and it is very satisfying when we are able to use the magazines to help people find out elusive information about a long lost relative.

Helen Grove, Librarian
London Transport Museum

08 Plans and drawings

Our engineering drawings collection has around 45,000 items. These include architectural, civil and mechanical engineering drawings covering stations, bridges, tunnels, track, the original electric tramway network, London Transport road and rail vehicles of all kinds and street and station furniture.

Access to the original items in this collection is restricted as many of them are large and fragile. Meticulously drawn by skilled draughtsmen, the plans are often as artistically pleasing as they are historically significant. Transport engineers still consult our drawings when stations are being refurbished. A growing number of the more significant plans are being photographed or scanned for easy reference access, and some examples are shown here.

Plan, section and elevation drawings of Gloucester Road station, Metropolitan District Railway, c1868

The Metropolitan District Railway — commonly known as 'the District' — was the second underground railway in London. It opened in 1868, following the original 1863 Metropolitan Railway. Gloucester Road station was on the first section of the District to open in 1868. John Fowler was engineer for both railways and was responsible for these plans. The iron and glass roof shown here was removed in 1905 and the platforms rafted over with masonry but the main station entrance building has been preserved and renovated.

1995/297

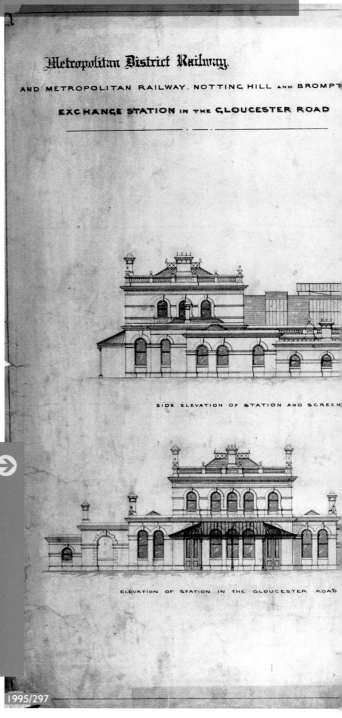

Metropolitan District Railway.

AND METROPOLITAN RAILWAY, NOTTING HILL AND BROMPT

EXCHANGE STATION IN THE GLOUCESTER ROAD

SIDE ELEVATION OF STATION AND SCREEN

ELEVATION OF STATION IN THE GLOUCESTER ROAD

1995/297

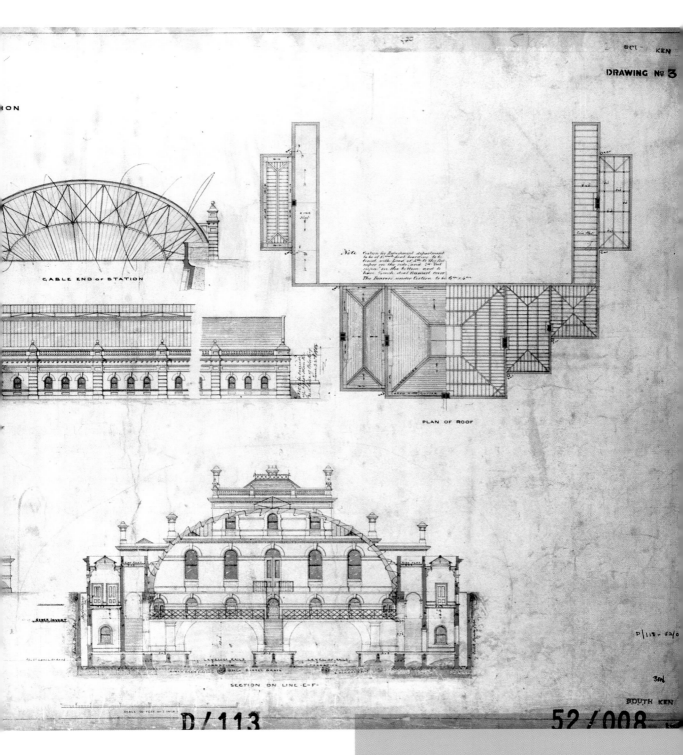

SCI-KEN

DRAWING No 3

GABLE END OF STATION

PLAN OF ROOF

SECTION ON LINE E-F

SCALE 30 FEET = 1 INCH

D/113

52/008

SOUTH KEN

1998/36010

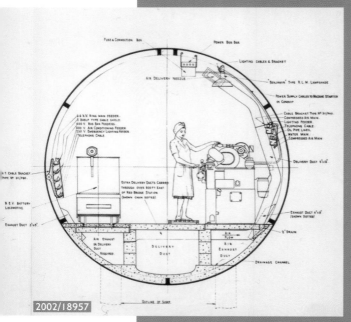
2002/18957

Sectional drawing of the secret Plessey tunnel factory, 1942

In 1939, at the start of the Second World War, new Tube tunnels for the eastern extension of the Central line were completed but not yet opened. The five mile section between Leytonstone and Gants Hill was turned into a secret factory for the Plessey company, producing aircraft components. This sectional drawing through one of the circular cast iron tunnels shows a woman at her workbench on the right, the air conditioning ducts and the miniature railway for carrying materials. The Central line extension was finally opened in 1947, after the war had ended.

2002/18957

Architect's drawing of Sudbury Hill station by Charles Holden, 1931

Frank Pick, managing director of the Underground Group and his favoured architect Charles Holden went on a study tour of Germany, Holland and Scandinavia in 1930 to look at civic and commercial buildings they both admired. Modern northern European architectural styles had a strong influence on Holden's Underground station designs for the Piccadilly line extensions in 1931-33. Here is his first elevation drawing for Sudbury Hill station, which is typical of what Holden called his 'brick box with a concrete lid' style. Frank Pick took a personal interest in the design of each station. Consequently this drawing, along with all of Charles Holden's architectural drawings, bears Frank Pick's signature.

1995/348

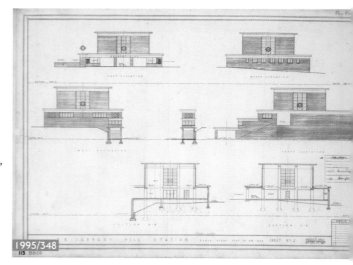
1995/348

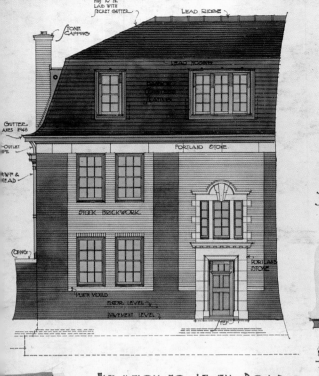

· ELEVATION · TO · LEVEN · ROAD ·

1999/20057

Architectural elevation of foreman's house, Poplar tram depot, London County Council Tramways, 1905

The Architects' department of the London County Council took as much trouble over their new tramway buildings in the 1900s as they did with their early housing estates, schools and fire stations. These beautifully detailed plans are for staff accommodation at Poplar tram depot. The foreman lived on site, looking after 96 trams in a big 'car shed', with a large stores and supplies yard alongside. By 1914 the LCCT system was the biggest electric tram network in the world.
1999/20057, 1998/84181, 1998/52479

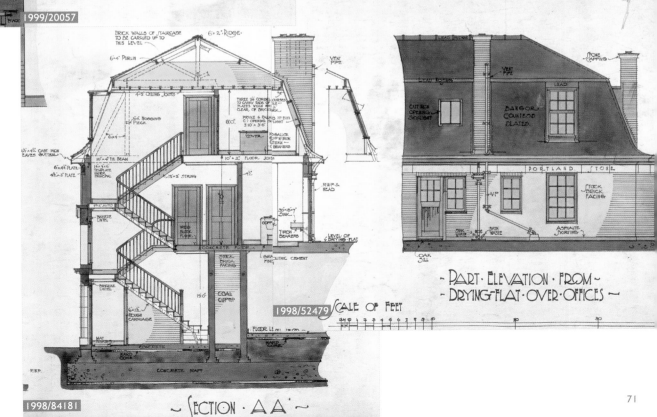

1998/52479

~ SCALE OF FEET ~

~ PART · ELEVATION · FROM ~
~ DRYING · FLAT · OVER · OFFICES ~

1998/84181

~ SECTION · A A ~

ARRANGEMENT OF 56 SEATER DOUBLE DECK BUS (Central)
Approved Colour Scheme.

2014/8439

TYPE S.T.L II

DRAWING No BP. 103/1

Approved colour scheme for an STL type bus, c1946
This is a page from a hand-painted livery specification book
prepared at Chiswick Works around 1946. After six years of
wartime austerity and bombing, London Transport faced a
huge task repairing and refurbishing its rundown and damaged
bus fleet. The STL type shown here had been the standard
double deck type in the 1930s and was due to be replaced by
the RT type from 1947. We have examples of both bus types
in the Museum collection.

2014/8439

The giant 'Aldenham Works'
lettering from the building
was saved and is now
displayed at the Depot.
You can see more examples
of our signage heritage in the
Maps and Signage collection.

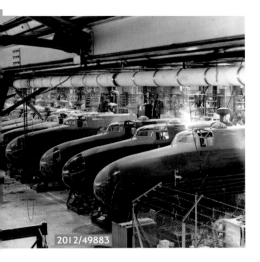

2012/49883

Diagram of Halifax bomber fuselage assembly by London Aircraft Production, 1942

London Aircraft Production (LAP) was a wartime group operation set up by the London Passenger Transport Board (LPTB) and four partners to build Handley Page Halifax heavy bombers, on eight different sites. Factory No. 2 was at Aldenham in Hertfordshire, in a building originally designed to be a depot for the planned extension of the Northern line beyond Edgware. LAP built 710 bombers here with a newly recruited workforce, mostly women with no previous engineering experience. After the war, Aldenham was enlarged to become London Transport's main bus overhaul works. It eventually closed in 1986 and was demolished.

2002/17898

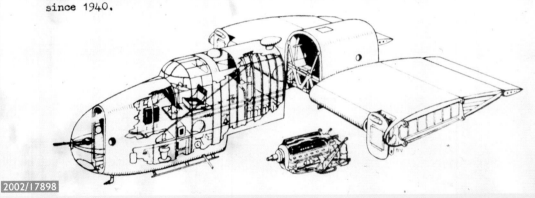

★ L.P.T.B. Factory No 2 ★

The assembly and installation of the Centre Section, and the installation of the Front Fuselage and Engines are carried out in this factory.

The No. 2 factory was intended for the housing and maintenance of Underground trains and was in course of construction at the commencement of the war. The factory has been adapted to its present purpose since 1940.

2002/17898

Diagram of a Halifax bomber fuselage assembly, 1942

One of my areas of research is 20th century conflict, so I was fascinated to discover that London Transport built heavy bombers during the Second World War. When people think of wartime London and the transport system, the first thing to spring to mind tends to be the image of people sheltering in the Underground during the Blitz, or of women working as conductors on the buses. But London Transport's involvement with the war effort went much deeper. This diagram represents the crucial role played by the organisation in manufacturing and engineering for the war effort.

Victoria Kingston, Researcher
Imperial War Museum

Arrangement of body structure for RM Routemaster bus, 1958

This sectional drawing shows the influence of aircraft construction methods on the design of the Routemaster. The bus has a lightweight aluminium body frame so, unlike earlier buses, it does not need a heavy chassis underneath to give it structural strength. Assembly involved simply bolting the body to front and rear axles. This bus was mass produced at the AEC and Park Royal Vehicles plants in west London between 1958 and 1968. The production version of the Routemaster varied from the initial prototypes in bonnet design and size.

2000/4723

Two of the Routemaster prototypes can be seen in the Museum's road vehicles collection.

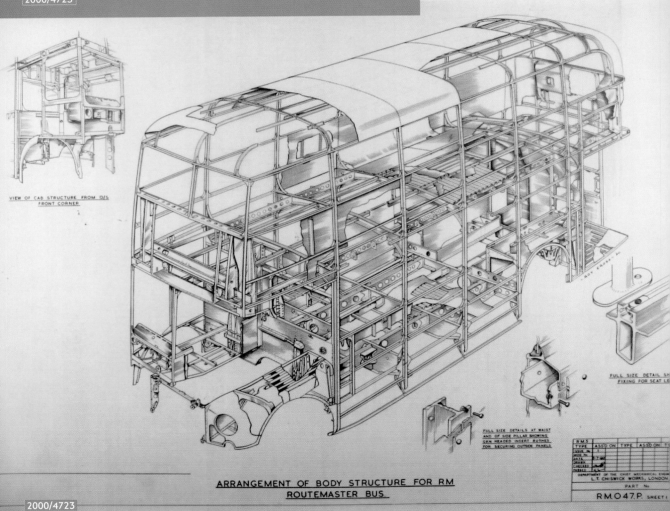

VIEW OF CAB STRUCTURE FROM O/S
FRONT CORNER

FULL SIZE DETAIL SH
FIXING FOR SEAT LE

FULL SIZE DETAILS AT WAIST
AND OF SIDE PILLAR SHOWING
GEN HEADED INSERT BUSHES
FOR SECURING OUTSIDE PANELS

ARRANGEMENT OF BODY STRUCTURE FOR RM
ROUTEMASTER BUS.

DEPARTMENT OF THE CHIEF MECHANICAL ENGIN
L.T. CHISWICK WORKS, LONDON

RM.O47.P SHEET I

2000/4723

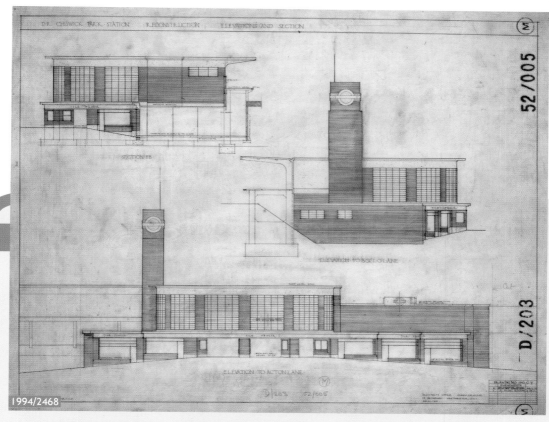

1994/2468

1994/2472

Station plan drawing of Chiswick Park station by Charles Holden, 1930s

As a teenager, I fell in love with Art Deco design. This passion was ignited by the opening of Biba in the 1960s, the fabulous fashion store in High Street Kensington. At the same time I began to notice the Art Deco architecture scattered around the London Underground network, with stations like Southgate, Arnos Grove and Chiswick Park. I moved to Chiswick Park in the late 1970s and I had the pleasure of using that iconic station on my daily commute. I subsequently discovered Charles Holden's station plan drawings in the Museum's collection, deepening my appreciation of this wonderful building. It is my fervent hope that one day it can be fully restored to its original glory, as shown in this blueprint which always gives me great joy.

Mike Walton,
Head of Trading and Poster Art Commissioner
London Transport Museum

London Transport Museum's collections include over 5,000 poster designs and 2,000 artworks, commissioned by London Transport and its predecessor and successor companies. Most are stored at the Depot, but they can all be seen on the website in **Collections online**.

From the first illustrated poster in 1908, Frank Pick and later London Transport was committed to employing the best of both established and emerging artistic talent in the service of the company. The posters represent a remarkable cross-section of artists and a huge range of styles, formats and techniques. There are posters to inform, posters to educate, posters to reassure, posters to entertain and posters to inspire. Some are targeted at London's daytime commuters, while many others encourage off-peak travel. The posters have always been a key element in a wider vision of 'total design' across London Transport that also takes in signage, typefaces, maps and station design. The poster and artwork store opens regularly for special tours. See our website for details.

1983/4/7

No Need to Ask a P'liceman!

John Hassall, 1908

This is the first graphic poster commissioned by the Underground Group. It was intended to highlight how simple it is to travel on the newly integrated Underground network – shown in the featured map – and takes its inspiration from the popular music-hall ballad 'Ask a P'liceman'. The finished poster differs from the artwork in broadening out the view to include a station and adding a slogan supplied by the schoolboy winner of a newspaper competition. Hassall was a well-known cartoonist and poster designer who also worked for Colman's Mustard and Nestles. In 1908, he famously created the 'Skegness is So Bracing!' image for the Great Northern Railway.

1983/4/7

The Way for All
Alfred France, 1911

Early poster advertising aimed to increase revenue by showing that everyone could travel by Underground including middle-class women, such as this one, travelling independently. The slogan and the frieze of passengers behind her reinforce this message of the democracy of Underground travel. The colour scheme of this poster — green, purple and white — was surely intended to echo those used by the women's suffrage movement. The original artwork was modified so that in the poster, the woman is less direct in her gaze, no longer catching the viewer's eye.

1983/4/124

1983/4/124

By Bus to the Pictures Tonight
Tom Eckersley and Eric Lombers, 1935

This small panel poster was one of the first joint commissions for Eckersley and Lombers, who met as art students in Salford, north-west England. In 1985, Eckersley became the first artist to celebrate 50 years of working for LT with a one-man retrospective exhibition at the London Transport Museum. Using public transport to enjoy the bright lights of the city has been a recurring theme in poster design through the decades. Some encourage off-peak travel in the evenings and at weekends, while others suggest that commuters delay their return home until after the rush hour.

1983/4/9728

International Advertising Exhibition
Frederick Charles Herrick, 1920

After the restrictions of the First World War, the Underground revived its graphic posters in 1920. This poster is peopled by characters used to advertise popular brands of the time – the Michelin Man and Johnny Walker are still in use today. The next two decades would be the golden age of poster design, both in quality and quantity. The transport system grew rapidly, and under the management of Frank Pick, a clear design identity encompassed everything from publicity to station design. The Underground Group commissioned work from both leading and emerging artists, with pioneering approaches to poster design.

1983/4/1240

1983/4/1240

Highgate Ponds
Howard Hodgkin, 1989

Begun in 1986, the 'Art on the Underground' scheme aimed to revive the tradition of commissioning work directly from artists to be reproduced on posters. These posters also helped fill the gaps left by unsold advertising space on the Underground. The posters were given a form of consistency as their subjects were inspired by potential destinations or leisure activities reached by Tube. Howard Hodgkin, an internationally famous painter and printmaker, was one of the best-known artists commissioned under this scheme.

1999/43124

Power – the Nerve Centre of London's Underground
Edward McNight Kauffer, 1930

American-born Kauffer, 'The Poster King', was the most prolific artist who worked for London Transport, designing over 100 posters. He was a leading champion of modernism in Britain and his studio was a meeting point for students and designers in exile from mainland Europe. This striking image celebrating London Underground's power station at Lots Road in Chelsea shows the modernist qualities of bold angular shapes and the incorporation of lettering into his design.

1983/4/2996

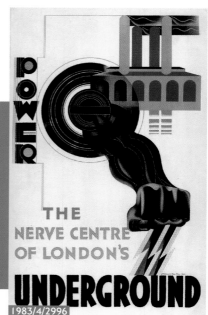

1983/4/9213

Trooping the Colour
Margaret Calkin James, 1932

The simplified and repeated forms on this poster for the annual Trooping the Colour ceremony, which celebrates the birthday of the monarch, show the influence of Calkin James's parallel work in textile design. A copy of this poster was presented to Queen Elizabeth II when she visited Baker Street for the 150th anniversary celebrations of the Underground in 2013. Calkin James was one of a number of women designers employed by London Transport between the two world wars. Others included Herry Perry and Dora Batty who produced over 50 posters each for the Underground.

1983/4/9213

Please Stand on the Right
'Fougasse' (Cyril Kenneth Bird), 1944

During the Second World War, many newcomers to London were unused to travelling on the Underground. This poster is one of a series designed to inform them about Tube etiquette, and it works in a more humorous way than the rather strident government information posters. Fougasse (the name of a small, improvised landmine) was the pseudonym of Cyril Kenneth Bird, one of Britain's most influential illustrators. His wartime work for the Ministry of Information included the famous 'Careless Talk Costs Lives' series.

1983/4/5709

1983/4/5709

LONDON

REGENT'S PARK

⊖ **Underground to Baker Street, then Bus 74**

1983/4/8041

© Estate of Abram Games and TfL from the London Transport Museum collection

London 2026 AD – this is all in the air

I really like this 1926 poster called London 2026 AD – this is all in the air, by Montague Black, because it is such an amazing vision of the future. Imagine looking at this poster in 1926, when St Paul's Cathedral was still the tallest building in the city. What's remarkable is how accurate some of Black's predictions turned out to be. The posters in the London Transport Museum collection were designed to be seen by ordinary people like you and me, encouraging them to travel more frequently and make the most of what the city has to offer. The poster collection gives us a bright and colourful, though often idealised, window onto past lives, a world that we now often know only through black and white film and photographs.

Anna Renton, Senior Curator
London Transport Museum

London Zoo
Abram Games, 1976

Games' personal design philosophy 'Maximum meaning, minimum means' was particularly suited to poster design. His first commission from London Transport was in 1937 and 40 years later this tiger created from the deconstructed shapes of the London Transport roundel was his last. London Zoo features on more London Underground posters than any other subject, despite being a good walk from any Underground station!

1983/4/8041

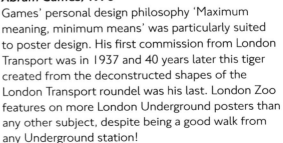

LONDON 2026 A.D.—THIS IS ALL IN THE AIR

TO-DAY — THE SOLID COMFORT OF THE UNDERGROUND

1983/4/3775

London after Dark
Fred Millet, 1968

In the 1960s and 1970s, the number of London Transport's direct poster commissions declined. The work was contracted out to agencies that typically preferred to use photographic images rather than artworks. These rarely matched the innovation and variety of previous campaigns. Fred Millet's collage is a rare venture by London Transport into Pop Art and captures the mood of London in the Swinging Sixties, just as that decade was coming to an end.

1983/4/7645

1983/4/555

3/4/7645

The Open Road; Fresh Air and Sunshine
Walter E Spradbery, 1914

This poster helped to establish the artist Walter Spradbery and he worked for London Transport for the next three decades. Leisure travel beyond central London was encouraged to fill empty seats and increase revenue during off-peak times. Posters advertised days out and leisure activities by Tube, bus or tram, or often a combination.

1983/4/555

 The B type bus shown in the poster is the same as the B types in the Museum's Road vehicles collection.

London Underground

Tube map platform art

DAVID SHRIGLEY

MAYOR OF LONDON   Transport for London

2006/13399

London Underground

Tube map platform art

MAYOR OF LONDON   Transport for London

2006/13403

Tube map covers, 2004-06

Since 2004, Art on the Underground has commissioned new works by contemporary artists for the front cover of the Pocket Tube map. A new one is produced about every six months. The examples featured here were commissioned between 2004 and 2006 and are by Emma Kay and David Shrigley. Each loosely re-interprets Henry Beck's famous Tube map of 1933. Other artists whose work has featured include Tracey Emin, Mark Wallinger and Cornelia Parker.

2006/13399, 2006/13403

Trevor Caley, Theatre Travelcard, mosaic artwork, 1986

The original artwork for London Transport's posters comes in many forms, sizes and style. This one, designed to advertise Travelcards, was originally a mosaic created by Trevor Caley. He has worked in a range of media but specialises in mosaic. In 1984–85 he collaborated with the sculptor Eduardo Paolozzi on the vibrant mosaics for the refurbished Tottenham Court Road Underground station.

1987/2

1987/2

1983/4/6117

London Transport at London's Service
Misha Black and John Barker, 1947

Pair posters, of which this is one half, were introduced after the Second World War. One half was for text, the other for the pictorial element. This allowed designers more artistic freedom and copywriters more space for text. The posters were positioned either side of station entrances. In the 1940s and early 1950s, London Transport's posters celebrated the city's resilience, while also asking for patience as the network struggled to repair wartime damage. The famous roundel first appeared on Underground platforms in 1908 and as its design evolved it was gradually rolled out across the London Transport network.

1983/4/6117

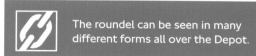

The roundel can be seen in many different forms all over the Depot.

1983/4/1745

Brightest London is best reached by Underground by *Horace Taylor*, 1924

To celebrate the 150th anniversary of the London Underground in 2013, the Museum held an exhibition called Poster Art 150 – London Underground's Greatest Designs. We invited the public to vote for their favourite in the Siemens Poster Vote and this was the winner. Brightest London was a worthy victor. It is eye-catchingly bright and vibrant, depicting London's stylish smart set heading for a night on the town by Underground. In an era of black and white films, the splash of colour must have been enthralling and the image would have been wonderfully aspirational for Londoners emerging from wartime austerity into the glamour of the 1920s. It also contains a little secret. The artist's granddaughter once explained that Taylor often included himself in his posters – here he is the gentleman with the top hat and beard on the middle escalator.

Wendy Neville, Head of Communications
London Transport Museum

The Museum's photograph, film and oral history collections record the operation of London's public transport organisations, the lives and experiences of their staff, the vehicles, streets and skyline of the city they serve, and the people that use the system. Around 25,000 images from the photo collection, dating from the 1850s up to the present day, are searchable on our website. They represent a selection of the best examples from the much larger collection, which is stored at the Depot.

Our earliest film dates from 1910, and is included in the selection of our most popular films that can be viewed on the LTM website. Nearly all our films have been digitised to increase accessibility. The Museum has also been recording oral and video histories since 1984. We gather and preserve historical information by interviewing people about past events, their working lives, and passenger experiences. Excerpts are regularly used in exhibitions and publications and in collaborative projects with community groups and students.

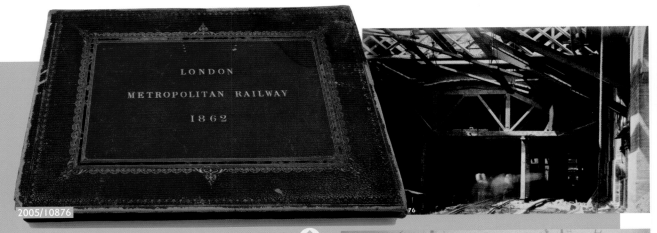

2005/10876

Metropolitan Railway construction album, 1862
This is our oldest original photo album, showing the construction of the world's first underground railway. It contains 39 prints showing work in progress at each station site, plus photographic copies of architectural drawings and a map of the route. The album was originally owned by Charles Gilpin, a Quaker MP and social campaigner, who was also a board member of the Metropolitan Railway.

2005/10876

1940s Carter colour slides

Images are held by the Museum in a wide range of formats. In 2010 we received a donation of early colour transparencies from the family of a noted amateur transport photographer, Clarence Carter. The slides were produced using the unusual Dufaycolor process and Carter processed them himself at home. The reds of London's buses, trams and trolleybuses are muted in these late 1940s and early 1950s shots, giving them a warm nostalgic quality.

2010/22485

LOLTM 2010/22485

2010/22485

2014/949

Olympic crowds outside Stratford station, 2012

The London 2012 Olympic and Paralympic Games presented the Museum with a great opportunity to capture London and its transport at a special moment in time. Photos and short informal interviews with spectators at Stratford and other Olympic sites helped to record the impact of the Games and contextualise the selection of signs, posters and leaflets that we collected during and after the events of summer 2012.

2014/949

Olympic Games crowds at Stratford station, photograph 2012

In 2012, I had the good fortune to curate an exhibition on the 1948 London Olympics. The capital had recently emerged from a bitter conflict that had left it bomb-damaged and its war-weary inhabitants rebuilding their lives. The late 1940s was an age of austerity and despite opposition to staging the Games, London succeeded in hosting the world's greatest sporting occasion. This photograph of relaxed visitors milling around Stratford station during the Games of 2012 is reminiscent of the images of thousands of excited Londoners making their way from patched-up stations to a converted Wembley Stadium in the summer of 1948.

Sian Flynn,
Curator of 'The Austerity Oympics', Farrer & Co, 2012

Films

Most of the 2,000 cans of raw material in the film store relate to the 65 films made for London Transport from the late 1940s to the early 1980s by British Transport Films, the UK's largest industrial film unit.

The construction of the Victoria line in the 1960s accounts for nearly a quarter of the total. The films were shown in cinemas before the main feature films, alongside other staples of the 'full supporting programme' such as cartoons and newsreels.

Glass negatives

Our collection includes about 50,000 glass plate negatives taken by the photo agency Topical Press. Between 1920 and 1958, different departments of the Underground Group (and later London Transport) commissioned Topical Press to take photos all over London for press and record-keeping purposes. Their subjects ranged from directors to cleaners, and included historic events as well as routine maintenance, technological and social change. A brief description of each negative was written into a series of bound log books kept by the agency, which are still consulted today. It took a team of volunteers two years to clean and wrap each individual plate.

1998/23441

St Paul's Cathedral, *photograph by Topical Press, 10 August 1944*

This photograph of St Paul's Cathedral shows the bomb damage sustained by surrounding buildings during the Second World War. It was the original photo on which Walter Spradbery based his 1944 poster, *The Proud City – St Paul's Cathedral* (see right), one of a series of six posters celebrating London's resilience during the Second World War. He intended to convey, in his own words 'the sense that havoc itself is passing and with new days come new hopes'. Other London landmarks in the series included the Tower of London and Parliament.

1998/23441

THE PROUD CITY

"the principal Ornament of our royal City, to the Honour of our Government, and of this our Realm."

1983/4/5766

 The full set of six posters can be seen in the Museum's poster collection, at the Depot and online.

Oral history recording, Winston Husbands, 1994

Oral history interviews are conducted by curators, but also by volunteers, the London Transport Museum Friends and other groups. Son of a fisherman and seamstress in Barbados, Winston Husbands left school aged 19 in 1961 and came straight to London as part of a London Transport direct recruitment programme in the Caribbean. He worked as a bus conductor out of Camberwell garage for thirty years, and was interviewed there in 1994 as part of a project celebrating London Transport's West Indian workforce. This studio portrait shows him in 1961 soon after arriving in London.

1996/2728

1996/2728

2005/9753

Jennifer Smith, Routemaster conductor
photograph by Julia Spiegl, 1989

This photograph was commissioned by the Museum as part of an exhibition project, recording bus driver and conductor crews at work, at a time when initial plans for the withdrawal of the Routemaster bus fleet were on the table. It was soon clear however, that the Routemasters built in the 1950s and 1960s, were in better shape than the more modern buses intended to replace them and many continued in service, with new engines, until 2005.

2005/9753

Examples of staff uniforms, and Gibson ticket machine No 366940 – the last Gibson in official company use on 21 August 1993 – can be seen in our small object collection.

Photograph of Tottenham Court Road station, 1946

The Topical Press photographers commissioned to record London Transport's everyday activities were given a reasonable amount of artistic licence in their work. Each day they had a list of jobs, and they delivered some great work. I particularly like this image of a man walking through a passageway at Tottenham Court Road tube station in July 1946. Although this was a fairly mundane request to show commercial advertising at a typical Underground station, the photographer's attention to details such as lighting and composition lift the image out of the ordinary, giving it a haunting, mysterious atmosphere. It fulfils the brief, while also hinting at the mood of a still from a 1940s film.

Simon Murphy, Curator
London Transport Museum

1998/45689

Florence Cordell, oral history, 1985

Florence was one of our earliest interviewees and the first to be recorded on video. She worked as a bus conductor during the First World War (see photo on page 36) and provided many insights into the period. While the leg gaiters she was required to wear as part of her uniform were 'a blinking nuisance', she greatly enjoyed the work, and especially the wages, which were much better than in her previous job in a lampshade factory.

2006/2611

2006/2611

All That Mighty Heart
British Transport Films, 1963

Much of the classic London Transport film *All That Mighty Heart* was shot by David Watkin, a cinematographer with a great eye for detail who later earned an Oscar for his work on David Lean's *Out of Africa*. This memorable image starts as a familiar shot of the lights of Piccadilly Circus at night, before the camera pans around to reveal a group of young people on the top deck of a bus.

2002/16366

2002/16366

2001/15373

Hainault Underground station booking hall colour transparency by Oliver Green, c1982

As part of our ongoing contemporary photography programme, we try to photograph collection items in their original context or in service, before they come to us. This shot of the booking hall at Hainault on the Central line in the early 1980s is by the Museum's then Head Curator. It includes the 1940s passimeter (an island ticket office) designed by Charles Holden, which we formally acquired in 1986.

2001/15373

 The passimeter and other examples from the 1920s and 1930s can be seen in the large object collection.

Built and operated by volunteers, the London Transport Miniature Railway (LTMR) is a 7¼ inch (184mm) gauge railway located in the grounds of the Museum Depot at Acton. During Depot Open Weekends, the railway provides popular rides with a variety of miniature rolling stock. The railway opened in 2005 during the Museum's 'London Transport in Miniature' Open Weekend. A dedicated team of volunteers maintain the railway, which includes a carriage shed, ticket office, sidings, passing places, and an impressive signalling system. Each year sees new additions and improvements.

london transport museum friends

In opening up the **Depot** to visitors, the Museum has the support of an enthusiastic group of volunteers in the **London Transport Museum Friends**

If you are visiting the Depot at an Open Weekend, you will see Friends working as volunteers throughout the site helping to explain the collections. Many of the displays at the Depot have been developed by the Friends themselves, including new exhibits which explain technical developments such as Underground signalling and train design.

Outside you can ride on the popular London Transport Miniature Railway and on one of the buses from the Museum's heritage vehicle collection — all brought to you through the efforts of the Museum Friends and other volunteers.

If you come to one of the monthly Depot tours, it is likely that you will be shown round by one of the knowledgeable volunteer guides.

All year round, Friends help to look after and expand the Museum collections. The Friends have been involved in major fundraising for vehicle restorations, including the District

line Q-stock train, the Metropolitan Railway 'Jubilee' carriage No. 353, the 1931 'Scooter' single deck bus LT 1076 and the First World War B type Battle Bus. The Friends have also provided funding for additions to the Museum's poster and other collections.

Behind the scenes, the Friends' activities include cataloguing new material and keeping the exhibits in a clean and presentable condition.

As well as these hands-on activities, Friends enjoy a programme of meetings and talks on transport-related subjects, as well as site visits and outings to venues across the Capital and beyond.

The London Transport Museum Friends is a membership charity, which works closely with the Museum to support its aims and collections. If you want to know more about becoming a Friend and getting closer to London's transport heritage, please visit the website **ltmuseumfriends.co.uk**

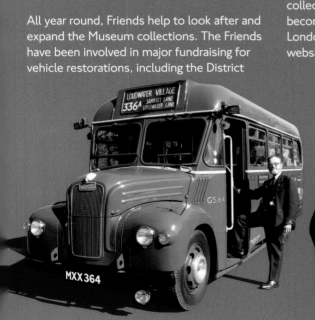

1983/4/2320

Shopping at the Depot

The Depot offers visitors a great range of shopping opportunities. The shop is packed with gifts, souvenirs, models, toys, posters, books and other great products. Many items are produced especially for London Transport Museum, including bags and cushions made from the original moquette seating fabric used on all Transport for London vehicles today.

At Depot Open Weekends we often have discounts or special offers and sometimes we sell original decommissioned items from London's transport system.

The London Transport Museum Friends also run a special stand at Open Weekends where you can buy original signs, timetables and other rare and unusual items and memorabilia. Independent, specialist retailers of books, models and other transport material also sell their products at our Open Weekends.

For a full range of products, including web-only merchandise, visit the London Transport Museum online store: **ltmuseumshop.co.uk**

Museum as a charity

London Transport Museum is a heritage and education charity, the world's leading museum of urban transport and a window on the past, present and future of transport in London.

Our purpose is to ignite curiosity to shape the future. We believe that our collections, stories and experiences can help everyone to understand more about the world they live in.

We look after more than 500,000 objects and every year welcome over 400,000 visitors to the Museum in Covent Garden and the Depot at Acton. Through exciting and interactive new galleries, temporary exhibitions, learning and public programmes, we create experiences that delight and inspire.

- We seek to educate the public about the wide role of transport in the life and work of London past, present and future.

- We help people develop skills for future employability, particularly in transport and engineering, and promote research about London, a city of global significance.

- We stimulate creativity from an early age and inspire the next generation to realise their potential.

- We are committed to provoking debate and imagination about transport and the future of London.

For more information on our heritage and education work visit **www.ltmuseum.co.uk**

London Transport Museum at Covent Garden

There is much more to discover at London Transport Museum in the heart of Covent Garden where our fully accessible galleries, lively displays, interactive exhibits, and a programme of exhibitions and activities tell the fascinating story of transport in London – past, present and future.

On permanent display at Covent Garden you can see trains, trams, buses, posters, artworks and key items from all our collections. Highlights include London's first horse bus, a steam locomotive used on the Circle line, a Victorian horse tram, the world's first electric underground locomotive, Henry Beck's original design for London's famous Tube map, a 1910 tram and 1930s trolleybus, and our popular Tube train driving simulator in the Future Engineers gallery.

The Museum's contemporary and future galleries showcase changes that are coming soon to London and give visitors the opportunity to think about what travel might be like in years to come. There are dedicated learning and play areas for children, and at weekends and during school holidays we offer special family trails and other activities. These include craft workshops, storytelling sessions and the opportunity to handle items from our wonderful collection.

The Museum's exhibition schedule changes every year as we explore different aspects of London's transport story and showcase our diverse collections. Exhibitions are accompanied by a varied programme of talks and events that expand on the ideas and themes behind the exhibition. Check the Museum website for the latest information about current and upcoming exhibitions, family activities, talks, and late-night openings.

Shopping

The Covent Garden shop stocks a range of innovative and exciting items including exclusive merchandise inspired by the Museum's collections and exhibitions. The shop is open daily and can be accessed directly from Covent Garden Piazza without purchasing a Museum ticket.

A full range of products including web-only merchandise is available at our online store **ltmuseumshop.co.uk**

Eating

The Upper Deck café above the main entrance offers a great selection of hot and cold food and drinks throughout the day. The menu includes transport-themed cocktails, shakes and smoothies. The Lower Deck café is located in the main Museum galleries. It opens at weekends and during school holidays offering a range of sandwiches, snacks and drinks. There is also a small picnic area inside the Museum where visitors can eat their own packed lunches.

Visiting

The Museum is open every day (except 24-26 December). Children and young people aged 17 and under go free. Adult admission tickets allow unlimited daytime entry to the Museum galleries and special exhibitions for a whole year. Save money by booking in advance online at **www.ltmuseum.co.uk**. Talks, events, late night openings, heritage vehicle outings, Depot Open weekends and tours are ticketed separately. See the Museum website for latest details.

Discover more

There are many ways in which you can explore the collections at London Transport Museum to find out more about London's public transport – past, present and future.

At the Depot there are monthly tours as well as Open Weekends. Heritage vehicle events at different locations on both rail and road are advertised on the Museum website, along with exclusive **Hidden London** tours to disused Underground stations. You can also enjoy talks at the Museum and other events out on the network.

Research online

Collections online provides access to over 270,000 records. Discover the collection by exploring twenty-two different collection types including vehicles, posters, photographs, maps, tickets, drawings, film and video, and sound collections. Learn about the people connected with the collections including staff, artists, designers and architects who worked for London Transport. You can also browse a selection of Library records. There are many ways to search the collection; by collection type, free text search, using advanced searches and sorting results using filters.

The Museum is continually developing different ways to access our collections online. New records and images are added every week and existing records are updated. Ultimately, we aim to provide access to all our catalogue records, except those restricted for copyright or privacy reasons.

https://www.ltmuseum.co.uk/collections/collections-online

Research at the Library

If you would like to do some research, you can visit the Library. It is open by appointment two days a week at Albany House in Petty France, near St. James's Park Underground station. Information about the kind of material we hold in the collection, including details of journals, reading lists and other resources, is on the Library page on the Museum website.

https://www.ltmuseum.co.uk/collections/research/library
Tel: +44 (0)20 7126 1022
Email: enquiry@ltmuseum.co.uk

Research at the Depot

The Depot at Acton holds the main collections of vehicles, signs, posters, artworks, photographs, ephemera, plans, drawings and small objects. Most collections are accessible for research but not all. If you are interested in specific material you need to email us with your request giving as much information as you can, and include a contact number. If access is possible, an appointment can be made to visit and look at material with a Curator on one of the days set aside for this purpose. See the website for more details.

Email: collections@ltmuseum.co.uk

Glossary

Bullseye or roundel
The bar and circle symbol used by London Underground evolved from the bar and disc design introduced in 1908. Edward Johnston re-designed the symbol during the 1920s to incorporate his new font. It was then known as the bullseye and became the official symbol of London Transport in 1933. The bullseye was renamed the 'roundel' in 1972 following an internal design review. The roundel is still the symbol of Transport for London (TfL) today.

Car or carriage
When electric underground trains were introduced in the early 1900s, the individual vehicles making up a train were always referred to as 'cars' rather than carriages. This followed American usage, as the open saloon interiors without compartments were similar to trains in the USA. Electric trams were also called 'cars' in both countries. In the UK this was short for tramcar and in the USA for streetcar.

Central London Railway (CLR)
The CLR, now part of the Central line, opened in 1900 between Shepherd's Bush and Bank. There was initially a flat fare of 2d which led to its popular nickname the 'Twopenny Tube'. It became part of the Underground Group in 1913.

City & South London Railway (C&SLR)
The City & South London Railway, opened in 1890, was the first deep level electric tube railway in the world, running from Stockwell to King William Street in the City of London. It was later extended and completely reconstructed, and today forms part of the Northern line.

Chassis
A chassis is the rigid frame of a vehicle onto which the body, motor, transmission and axles are fixed. Most cars today have lightweight 'integral' construction without a separate chassis, but heavier duty commercial vehicles like trucks usually still have the body structure built on to a chassis unit.

Conductor rails
Underground, Overground and Docklands Light Railway (DLR) trains are powered by conductor rails which carry electricity. London Underground uses a four rail system with two running rails and separate positive and negative electrified conductor rails. Power is picked up by collector shoes on the trains running along the rails. This system guards against current leakage in the tunnels and separates the signal control system through the running rails. On the Overground, DLR and national rail lines in south London, power supply is through a single conductor rail.

Driving motor car
Driving motor cars are motorised passenger cars with a driving cab which can be at the front or rear of a multiple unit train and driven from the controls at either end. They replaced the original electric locomotives on the C&SLR (City & South London Railway) and CLR (Central London Railway) Tubes. They were also used on early electric trains on the Metropolitan and District lines.

Gate stock
Tube trains introduced in the early 1900s were known as 'Gate stock' because of the entrance and exit system they used. There were no side doors on the vehicles, so passengers had to get on and off via an open gated platform at the end of each car. A gateman rode between the cars, opening and closing the gates manually at each station and shouting out the name of each station on arrival. It was a slow, cumbersome and labour intensive system. New trains with multiple air-controlled doors controlled by one guard replaced all the Gate stock in the 1920s.

Livery
The distinctive colour scheme of a road or rail vehicle, which identifies the transport company that owns it or a particular route that it runs on, is known as a vehicle's livery. These remained constant for many years, with London Transport's central area buses always painted red and its country buses green, for example.

Locomotive or engine
A railway locomotive or engine is a single item of rolling stock with its own power unit (steam, diesel or electric) which can pull carriages, cars or wagons along a track. A locomotive, or loco, plus carriages make a train.

London County Council Tramways (LCCT)
Starting in 1903, the London County Council Tramways (LCCT) created the largest electric tram system in the world. It became part of London Transport in 1933, and a tram replacement programme began in 1935, first with trolleybuses up to 1940, then with diesel buses after the Second World War. The last part of the LCCT system was closed in 1952.

London General Omnibus Company (LGOC)

The London General Omnibus Company (LGOC) was created in 1856 and soon became the largest operator of horse buses in London. Motor buses were introduced in the early 1900s, and with the development of the successful B type bus in 1910 the LGOC was able to replace all its horse buses in 1911. By 1912 the LGOC had become part of the Underground Group but the buses kept their bright red livery and 'General' fleet name. It was merged into London Transport in 1933.

London Transport (LT)

In 1933, a new public transport authority was created for London. Its full title was the London Passenger Transport Board (LPTB), soon after known as London Transport (LT). It was responsible for all bus, coach, tram, trolleybus and Underground railway operation in the London area, covering a 20-30 mile (32-48 km) radius from Charing Cross. Taxis, river boats and suburban rail services were excluded. LT went through various administrative changes and was eventually succeeded by Transport for London (TfL) in 2000.

London United Tramways (LUT)

London United Tramways (LUT) was a private company which operated the Capital's first electric tram services in the western suburbs in 1901. It became part of the UERL, introduced London's first trolleybuses in 1931 and eventually merged into London Transport in 1933.

Metropolitan Railway (the Met)

In 1863, the Metropolitan Railway opened the first underground railway in the world. It ran from Paddington to Farringdon using steam trains. It was extended to link up with the second underground line, the District in 1868, eventually creating the Circle line in 1884, and a main line running deep into London's north-west countryside in 1892. This outer area was promoted in the 1920s with new suburbs known as 'Metro-land'. In 1933 the Met was merged with the UERL during the creation of London Transport.

Moquette

Moquette is the hardwearing woollen fabric used to cover seats on all London buses and Underground trains since the 1920s.

Multiple unit control system

The multiple unit system was devised by Frank Sprague in the USA in the 1890s. It allows trains to be operated from either end, rather than having to move a locomotive from one end of the train to the other to run it in the opposite direction. With a multiple unit the driver simply walks from the cab at one end of the train to the other to make the return journey. Today all London Underground electric passenger trains are multiple units.

Stock or rolling stock

Rolling stock is the term used to describe all the vehicles that move on a railway, such as diesel and electric locomotives, passenger carriages and freight wagons.

Substation

Part of an electrical generation, transmission and distribution system, substations perform several important functions such as transforming electrical voltage from high to low, or the reverse.

Tramlink

Trams returned to Croydon, south London, in 2000 in modern 'light rail' form. The Tramlink network uses a combination of former suburban railway lines and newly built track.

Transport for London (TfL)

London Transport was replaced by Transport for London (TfL) in 2000. The new transport authority for the Capital reports to the Mayor of London and has much wider responsibilities than LT, including taxis, river services, strategic or main roads, bridges and cycling as well as buses, the DLR, Tramlink and LU. TfL has also established the London Overground network, refurbishing and linking up former suburban rail lines to create new orbital services around the city.

Tube / deep Tube

The 'Tube' was a popular nickname originally applied to the new deep level electric underground lines opened in London from 1900. It began as simple shorthand for the method of construction. A tunnel was dug by miners, and lined with curved iron segments bolted together to create a circular tube. Strictly speaking, these original shallow cut and cover lines on the Metropolitan & District lines are not part of the Tube network, but the name is commonly used today to refer to the whole of the London Underground system.

UNDERGROUND

UNDERGROUND was first used in 1908 as a brand name in distinctive lettering. At this time, the various lines were managed by separate private companies. They were in competition but saw the benefits of joint marketing and agreed to use this shared branding outside all stations and on free map guides to the whole system. By 1913 there were just two private companies, the Metropolitan Railway and the Underground Group, which both became part of a single public corporation, London Transport, in 1933.

Underground Electric Railways of London (UERL) or Underground Group

The Underground Electric Railways of London (UERL), also known as the Combine or Underground Group, was a private company set up in 1902 to build and operate the Tube network. By 1912 it had grown to become London's biggest transport operator, with subsidiary companies running buses, trams and underground railways.

Plan your journey

Directions
Use the TfL Journey Planner to plan your route
to the Museum Depot: **tfl.gov.uk**

London Transport Museum Depot
2 Museum Way
118–120 Gunnersbury Lane
London W3 9BQ
Tel: +44 (0)343 222 5000 (Museum switchboard)

Underground
Acton Town (District and Piccadilly line)

Buses
E3 to Gunnersbury Lane (Acton Town)
70, 207, 266, 607, H40 to Gunnersbury Lane/Uxbridge
Road junction

Parking
Limited parking is available to Blue Badge holders only,
on a first come first served basis.

Cycles
Cycles can be secured outside, in the Depot grounds.

Access
The London Transport Museum Depot is close to
Acton Town Underground station. The approach road
to the Depot has a fairly steep incline. Inside the Depot
there are ramps and wheelchair platforms to some
areas and a lift to the first floor. The disabled toilet is
on the ground floor. Some vehicles are accessible to
wheelchair users. A plan of the Depot can be found on
the page opposite.

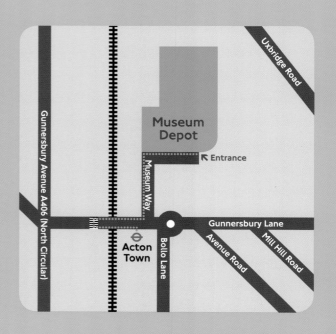

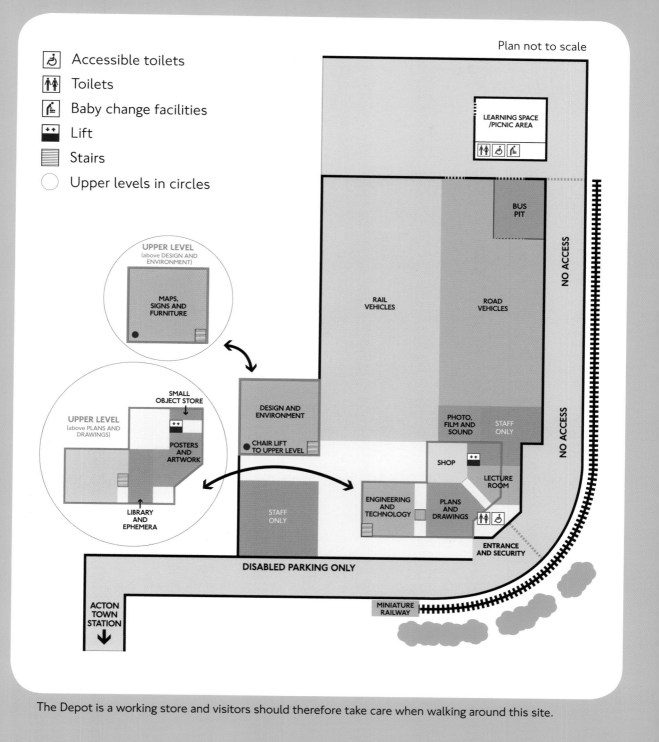

Plan not to scale

Legend:
- Accessible toilets
- Toilets
- Baby change facilities
- Lift
- Stairs
- Upper levels in circles

UPPER LEVEL (above DESIGN AND ENVIRONMENT)
MAPS, SIGNS AND FURNITURE

UPPER LEVEL (above PLANS AND DRAWINGS)
SMALL OBJECT STORE
POSTERS AND ARTWORK
LIBRARY AND EPHEMERA

LEARNING SPACE /PICNIC AREA

BUS PIT

NO ACCESS

RAIL VEHICLES

ROAD VEHICLES

DESIGN AND ENVIRONMENT

CHAIR LIFT TO UPPER LEVEL

PHOTO, FILM AND SOUND

STAFF ONLY

NO ACCESS

SHOP

LECTURE ROOM

STAFF ONLY

ENGINEERING AND TECHNOLOGY

PLANS AND DRAWINGS

ENTRANCE AND SECURITY

DISABLED PARKING ONLY

ACTON TOWN STATION

MINIATURE RAILWAY

The Depot is a working store and visitors should therefore take care when walking around this site.